CANALS

AND THEIR ARCHITECTURE

Excursions into Architecture

SERIES EDITOR

David Braithwaite

CANALS
AND THEIR ARCHITECTURE

Robert Harris

GODFREY CAVE ASSOCIATES
LONDON

First published in 1969
by Hugh Evelyn Limited
Second Edition 1980
Published by Godfrey Cave Associates Limited
© 1969 & 1980 Robert Harris

SBN 0 906223 20 2
SBN 0 906223 21 0

Designed by Sheila Sherwen
Printed and bound in Great Britain by
Morrison & Gibb Ltd, London and Edinburgh

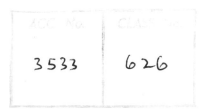

CONTENTS

INTRODUCTION

by Charles Hadfield

A love of canals is compounded of many ingredients. Most of us hold in our mind's eye, on such a February day as I write this, long ribbons of water that lie, faintly ruffled by the wind, under the soft English summer sky, enclosed by green banks, hedgerows and scattered trees. Along the towpath fishermen sit, watching, waiting, enjoying the silence, having circumvented their wives.

In the distance a motor cruiser makes its slow way down the canal, ripples spreading from its bows, a rolling splash of water following. On deck, I see myself sitting hour after hour, attentive to the countryside or the intervening town, but more to the endless detail of the unpretentious structures that move past – bridges, locks and their lock-houses, tunnels, aqueducts, warehouses or canalside pubs. They were created because they were needed, designed more in the mind's eye than on the drawing board, built by working craftsmen under engineers who had themselves been working craftsmen, and they fitted into a countryside emptier then of buildings.

Robert Harris is a romantic, and so am I. He loves forms, and has pictured them in his outstanding collection of illustrations. But he never loses sight, in text or pictures, of the theme, that canals obtained their forms as responses to necessities, as the result of the passion and imagination of their builders applied to practical problems. This being so, when necessities change, so do the visions of those who have to create the new forms they require.

Over the centuries there has been a continuing development of technique – of how to construct waterways for efficient use, and to raise craft from one level to another; how to build boats to carry as much as possible within a limited section, and move as fast as possible; how to organise goods carrying services; how to unload, store and keep cargo safe; how, very often, to provide passenger services, formerly for business, now for pleasure. Therefore canals, in Britain or abroad, are not museums of architecture, but ways of human activity at work or play, round which come and go the changing forms that embody it at one time or another. We can enjoy the canal architecture of the past, knowing that if we in turn do our work well, unpretentiously, to meet our present necessities, our successors will enjoy ours.

PREFACE

The foremost purpose of this work is to examine in some detail the machinery, the engineering structures and the buildings which have made possible the art of inland navigation: the architecture, in fact, of canals. For such examination to be comprehensive the briefest discovery must first be made of waterways themselves: short tracings through history to encounter the mechanics of canal evolution, the labours and the fermenting of ambition that was to become vision fulfilled.

It was the Romans who brought organised engineering to Britain, and the long, straight roads whose building they supervised were the island's first major transport routes between settlements. At the colonisers' departure, however, these great tracks became redundant; most were disused, overtaken by nature, and finally obliterated. It was not until the dawning of an industrial era that a unified transport system again became essential to connect Britain's naturally based communities for the purposes of efficient inland trade.

In many countries the construction of artificial navigable water channels was undertaken from earliest times to help river navigations; usually they avoided tortuous bends or rapids and shallows. It would be foolish to attempt to state where the first true navigable canal was built, for history is seldom complete. Canals, in the form of irrigation channels, existed in Egypt in 1350 BC. Some of these may also have been navigations. A plan to connect the River Nile to the Red Sea by a navigable channel was conceived in about 1300 BC but not completed until more than 800 years later. This canal was equipped with the earliest form of lock of which any record survives: 'Ptolemy the Second . . . caused to be constructed a dam or sluice which opened to give a passage, and immediately closed again.' (*European Magazine,* 1810.)

Britain excepted, the continent of Europe was not long without its several systems of inland navigation. Not surprisingly, considering the suitability of terrain, the art was to be perfected first in the Netherlands. The greatest feats of construction, however, were to be seen in France, on her Canal du Languedoc. Here, on an undertaking begun in 1666 with the aim of connecting the Atlantic and the Mediterranean, were 113 locks, many impressive aqueducts, and a tunnel 720 feet in length, part lined with freestone and part cut through solid rock.

It was to the European waterways, and to this 'Canal of the Two Seas' in particular, that a young English nobleman, the Duke of Bridgewater, with his tutor Robert Wood, came in 1753 to study and admire their exceptional works of engineering. There can be little doubt that the excitement imbued by these accomplishments was to be a driving force behind the Duke's own ventures into canal promotion which heralded the true founding of inland navigation in Britain. The story of these ventures and their consequences during the following decades involves men who were neither solely architects nor engineers, rather true pioneers of the Industrial Age.

Author's Note

Just a quarter of a century before the first publication of this book – in 1944 – a new era of canal literature was opened with L. T. C. Rolt's *Narrow Boat*. For me, *Narrow Boat* is still the best account of an introverted culture that has continued to evolve from the earliest days of the Industrial Revolution. My book remains dedicated to this, the culture of the working boatmen.

Nearly ten years have passed since the bulk of this material was assembled. During that time my waterways bookshelves have had to expand considerably to accommodate a flood of new material on the subject in general, although I must record that amongst all the picture-books, technical manuals, travelogues and souvenir guides very little other than of a journalistic nature has appeared to complement the particular subject here presented: the fabric of canals. The books of Charles Hadfield still form the foundation stone of British canal documentation today, and the enthusiast must be especially grateful to have so readily available works which unfold the fascinating story of a nation's canal development and which are always the result of extensive and detailed research. It was only through being able to call upon the writings of devoted historians past and present that it became possible to open this further chapter in the story of inland navigation.

Changes in the literature of canals over the decade are reflected in the revised bibliography. Physical changes have been, perhaps, more numerous, and sometimes unhappy – Telford's Ellesmere Port warehouses gone; Harecastle Tunnel closed $3\frac{1}{2}$ years for repair; use of the whole system severely restricted for months because of drought. . . . While out of it all a paradox arises: the enthusiasm of the 'new navvies', present-day volunteer canal builders, fired by such successful recoveries as Stratford, Ashton and Upper Avon, looks now to new horizons as apparently remote as Thames & Severn (closed 1911) and even Wilts & Berks (last used 1906 and in parts vanished) – but to what end? There seems to be as yet no parallel increase in the enthusiasm of carriers for water transport. Is the harvest of all this free labour to be reaped only by weekend boaters and hire fleet operators?

Illustrations are acknowledged separately, but I must here repeat my special thanks to those individuals and organisations who helped in the original compilation of this book, either by making material available, or by actively participating in my researches and photographic travels: my parents; Richard Baker; R. H. J. Cotton; Howard Diamond; Paul Dyson; W. A. Harmsworth; Leslie Harris; Antoni Kay; P. Myall; Richard Snell; Derrick Turner; Jim and Flo Woolgar; Russell Wootton; various departments of the British Waterways Board; Charles Hadlow, curator of the museum at Stoke Bruerne, and his successor, Richard Hutchings; the University of Liverpool; members of the Railway and Canal Historical Society, and libraries and record offices in many counties.

I spent the summer of 1967 in a most leisurely and enjoyable fashion, exploring the English Canal System, searching out the facts and folklore of its construction. 'Greywell' – once a ship's lifeboat – served me faithfully a few years more, then passed from my ownership. As I write this, she lies under northern waters, having been holed while crossing the Pennines!

I walk with old ghosts the banks of Wey & Arun, Thames & Severn, Wilts & Berks, awaiting the 'new navvies' and dreaming the romantic's dream of what these waters once were, and could be again: highways, not playgrounds – but also the garden of those whose homes were the painted boats.

Alton, June 1979   Robert Harris

Acknowledgements

The majority of the photographs, prints and engravings are from the Author's own collections. For the exceptions, acknowledgement and thanks are due to the following: Philip Roberts, for the loan of *Utensils in Canal Work,* a unique illustrated record of canal building during the late eighteenth century; Aerofilms p 145, p 179, p 180 (bottom); David Braithwaite p 79, p 202; British Waterways Board p 86 (left); Department of Transport, Canada, p 162; The Engineer p 181 (top); Mary Evans Picture Library p 55 (bottom); David Gerry p 130, p 163; Greater London Council p 60, p 138, p 165; L. E. Harris p 49 (bottom); Ironbridge Gorge Museum Trust p 192, p 196 (bottom); Hugh McKnight Photography p 28 (bottom), p 46, p 47 (left), p 65, p 146, p 167, p 169 (top); W. O'Grady p 124; Port of Manchester p 178, p 180 (top); David Robinson p 193, p 194, p 195; Richard Snell p 21, p 35 (top), p 102, p 126, p 196 (top); Strachan & Henshaw of Bristol pp 184–7; Surrey and Hampshire Canal Society p 112; Harold Tucker p 188; University of Liverpool p 149; Waterways Museum, Stoke Bruerne, p 115, p 168, p 182, p 183, p 198; Lady Elton for the colour plates opposite pp 80–1 and Hugh Street for those opposite pp 64–5.

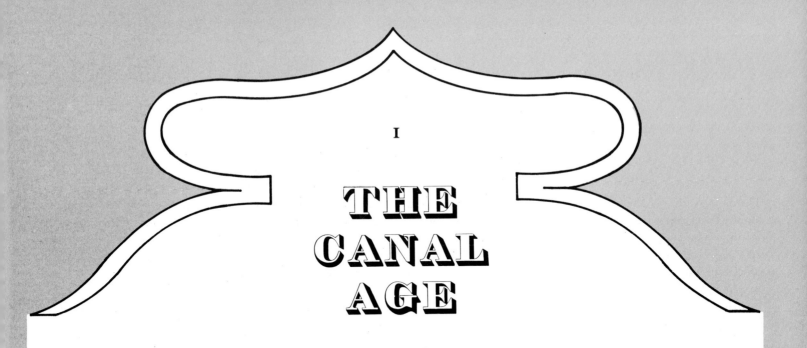

I

THE CANAL AGE

Accounts of inland navigation through Britain prior to the eighteenth century are sparse. Of canals and canal-building, few enough works were carried out, and fewer, undoubtedly, have left us any surviving record.

One of the earliest (but very prolific) historians who devoted himself entirely to the subject was J Phillips, whose standard work dates only from 1792: *A General History of Inland Navigation, Foreign and Domestic: containing A Complete Account of the Canals Already Executed in England; with Considerations on Those Projected.* Phillips' authority is unquestionable, for he once worked under James Brindley and therefore had first-hand knowledge of the founding of an English canal system.

Phillips was primarily concerned, as here, with his own contemporary canal age, but his study includes an outline of the pre-history of British canals, mentioning first the Roman Car Dyke, '. . . as it is the most ancient'. History has become considerably more complete since the time of Phillips, for, while he expresses doubt as to its navigable origin, it is now known that the Car Dyke, 56 miles long from the Nene to Witham, a few miles below Lincoln, was part of an extensive canal system providing through communication by water from the Cambridge area to York. The same system included the still extant Fosse Dyke, and was probably established by AD 60, passing out of use late in the second century. The Fosse Dyke is once more recorded as a navigation in the reign of Henry I, but not until 1780 was any major work executed on the canal,

Contrasting waterways:
Left The Thames at Abingdon,
near its junction with the defunct
Wilts and Berks Canal
Right Buildings beside the Trent
and Mersey Canal at Shardlow,
the first canal 'new town',
evolving at the junction of this
canal with the River Trent

when, together with the adjoining River Witham, it was widened and straightened to its present course, partly as a drain for the South Lincolnshire Fens but also because of the importance of a water route between the Trent, Boston and the Wash.

Phillips next mentions the remains of a canal from Sandown Castle in Kent to the sea, made in the time of Edward VI, but neglects altogether the far more important and still thriving Exeter Canal. This 5-mile waterway, built by John Trew of Glamorgan during the reign of Elizabeth I, was the first in Britain to use 'pound locks'. The limitations of these earliest devices are not now known but the canal today is able to pass vessels up to 120 feet long and 26 feet in width.

England's first 'modern' canal came about unintentionally in 1755, when an Act of Parliament was passed to make navigable the Sankey Brook from the River Mersey near Sankey Bridge to St Helens in Lancashire. It was decided, however, that the navigation was not practicable, and a completely artificial watercourse was opened in 1761 alongside the brook, several locks being provided to adapt the canal to the level of the lands passed through.

By coincidence, the new cut passed close to the estates of that same young nobleman who had so recently been examining enthusiastically the phenomenon of canal transport abroad.

The Duke's extensive coalfield at Worsley was at that time difficult to exploit economically, although the de-

Left Broad Waterway: the River Trent near Derwentmouth
Below Narrow waterway: locks at Audlem on the main line of the Shropshire Union Canal

manding manufactories of Manchester were less than eight miles distant, for the road conditions were bad and the cost of haulage was prohibitive. This was motive enough for the ambitious Francis Egerton to consider undertaking, himself, the yet novel enterprise of an English canal.

In 1759, Parliament passed an Act 'to enable the Most Noble Francis Duke of Bridgewater, to make a navigable Cut or Canal from a certain place in the township of Salford, to or near Worsley Mill, and Middlewood, in the manor of Worsley, and to or near a place called Hollin Ferry, in the county palatine of Lancaster'.

Here then, was the first great canal promoter, and here, too, his proud foundation of a water transport system that would carry a new revolution of industrialism through the middle lands of Britain. It was to be a powerful revolution, bringing prosperity to many, but poverty and misery to many thousands more. The Duke was the idealist, but the engineer who was to make a reality of his vision was of humbler origin.

James Brindley, 'Father of English Canals', was born in a remote hamlet in the High Peak of Derbyshire, 'in the midst of a rough country, then inhabited by quite as rough a people' (Smiles). In the year 1733, when he was 17, and still 26 years before John Gilbert, agent and planner of the Duke of Bridgewater's Canal, was to search out his genius, James began his career by being bound apprentice to Abraham Bennett, a wheelwright and millwright at the village of Sutton, near Macclesfield.

'The Most Noble Francis Duke of Bridgewater', 1736–1803

Millwrights were then the only engineers; in the course of their trade they worked at the lathe, the carpenter's bench and the anvil by turns, and so acquired practical knowledge of the strength and qualities of materials, and dexterity in the handling of all kinds of tools.

That Brindley's powers of observation and mental calculation were acute is left to no doubt. Although he had never had a formal education, even in reading or writing, and at his apprenticeship he was often entirely ignored by the millwright and his journeymen, within three years his workmanship and opinions were being sought in preference to those of the master himself, a situation which caused no little harm to the pride of the latter. 'Jem', his master complained, 'if thous goes on i' this foolish way o' warkin', there will be very little trade left to be done when thou comes oot o' thy time: thou knows firmness o' wark's th' ruin o' trade.' Neither was there consolation to be found from his inquiry of young James as to where he had obtained his knowledge of mill-work: '. . . it came natural-like', was the retort.

By 1742 the soundness of Brindley's work had rewarded him with his own wheelwright's business. This was at Leek, not far from the Staffordshire Pottery district, shortly to rise into importance through the energy and influence of Josiah Wedgwood. Brindley had taught himself to write (in a manner) and kept his own record books. In one of these we find entered a 'Loog of Daal 20 foot long' which was required for a flint-mill of a Mr Tibots, 'a mow

James Brindley, 1716–1772,
Britain's first canal engineer

'A Trawley or hand Carriage for Stone'.
From *Utensils in Canal Work,* a unique
book, written and drawn by hand by an un-
identified student of canal works. It is a
rare record of the building of a canal

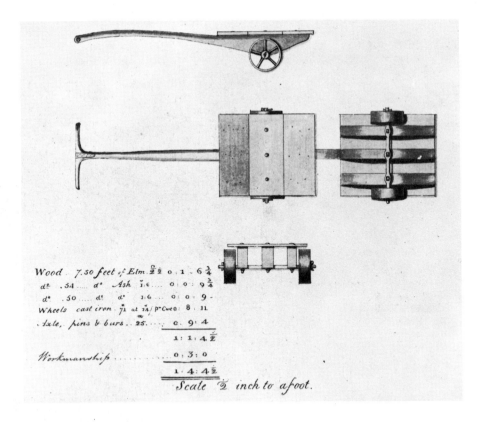

'Wheelbarrow of dimensions used upon
the Warwick & Bm Canals' – from
Utensils in Canal Work. The basic tools of
the navvy were pick, shovel and barrow

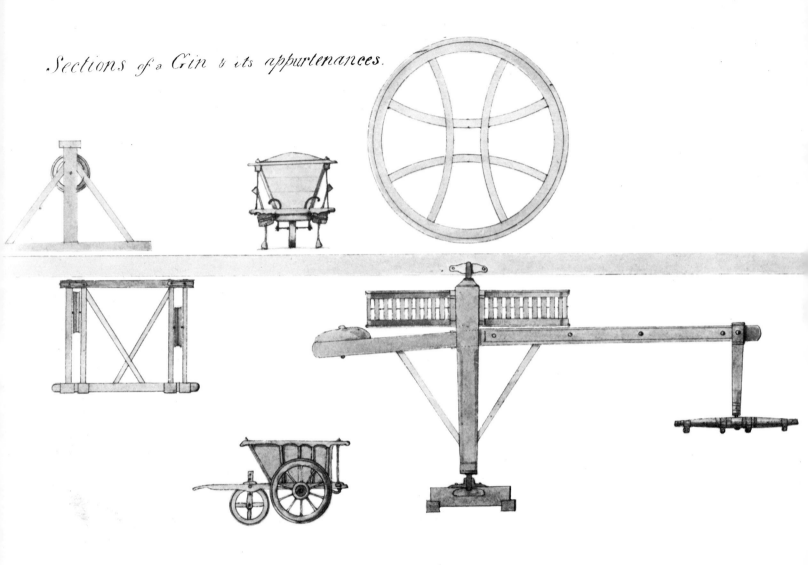

Sections of a Gin & its appurtenances.

Before the inception of steam power, horse gins were widely
used in civil engineering work. One of their many applications
in canal construction was the hauling of spoil buckets through
the vertical shafts of tunnel borings, from *Utensils in
Canal Work*.

Side & end views of Carts used upon the Warwick & Birmingham Canal for the purpose of conveying Soil &c from deep cutting to Embankments July 3rd 1794 —

Canal construction inevitably involved the moving of large amounts of soil both to and from the immediate workings, and these were often inaccessible to horse wagons. Laborious means of transport had then to be resorted to; this small hand-cart was, at best, an improvement on the wheelbarrow from *Utensils in Canal Work*.

invontion'. If this flint-mill was indeed a new invention then it was a valuable one, for the potters of the time were severely hampered by a short supply of flint-powder. Hence from that time forward the yet undiscovered canal engineer was frequently occupied in erecting flint-mills in Burslem and the neighbourhood.

In 1755, when powers were obtained to construct the Sankey Canal, the Corporation of Liverpool had under their consideration a much larger scheme, no less than a canal to unite the rivers Trent and Mersey and so open up a water route between the ports of Hull and Liverpool. Two surveys were made; the second, promoted by a Lord Gower, involved James Brindley on his first canal work, for we find the following entered by him in his records: on 5th February 1758, 'novocion 5 days'; on 19th February, 'a bout the novogation 3 days'; and again, 'surveing the novogation from Long brigg to Kinges Milles 12 days ½'. At this time, however, the canal from the Trent to the Mersey was to remain an exciting dream, and it was Lord Gower's brother-in-law, the Duke of Bridgewater, who next called upon the services of this wheelwright in connection with inland navigation.

While engaged on the planning of the Duke's canal, Brindley found time to continue with his work in the Potteries, giving attention to mills, water-wheels, cranes and 'fire-engines', and to survey a canal through Staffordshire. He also purchased a quarter-share of the Golden Hill estate at Turnhurst knowing this to be rich in minerals.

Cutting was commenced on the first section of the Duke's canal in 1760. Of how many men were employed at this time we have no record, nor are we certain from which classes these first 'navigators', the 'navvies' of today, were born. A general upheaval in the working populace was created during the early days of industry's advance. The manufactories were absorbing more and more of the hitherto dominant agriculturalists, and in spite of meagre wages and wretched conditions the labourers, too, hoped that the expanding townships might present to them a more opulent future. It is not unreasonable to suppose that many, unable to realise or support their ambitions in the mills or the mines, might have turned to a less oppressive, though equally harsh, employment in building the canals. Their tools were diminutive, only pick-axes, spades and barrows, but their task was gigantic – to cut an artificial waterway into Manchester.

Of the skilled labourers, Smiles is very informative:

Though there was at first a lack of skilled carpenters, blacksmiths, and bricklayers, they soon became trained into such under the vigilant eye of so expert a master as Brindley was. We find him, in his note-book, often referring to the men by their names, or rather byenames, for in Lancashire proper names seem to have been little used at that time. Black David was one of the foremen most employed on difficult matters, and Bill o' Toms and Busick Jack seem also to have been confidential workmen in their respective departments. Most of the labourers employed were of a superior class, and some

A Basingstoke Canal token, issued to labourers by the contractor, John Pinkerton, for exchange only at certain stores and public houses run by him; sailing barges were not in fact used on this canal

of them were *wise* or *cunning men,* blood-stoppers, herb-doctors, and planet-rulers, such as are still to be found in the neighbourhood of Manchester. Their very superstitions made them thinkers and calculators. The foreman bricklayer, for instance, as his son used afterwards to relate, always 'ruled the planets to find out the lucky days on which to commence any important work', and he added, 'none of our work ever gave way'.

The novel labour of these men was no less a discipline of self-instruction than was the art of canal building to Brindley himself. The Duke, it was true, had examined many of the wonders of waterways on the continent of Europe and the very existence of these must have given him faith in the practicality of his ideas, but his engineer had not even the small advantage of viewing these precedents. Each problem was overcome as it arose, by the application of his still limited knowledge, his technical experience and his uncomplicated sense of logic. It is said of him that whenever difficulties did arise he would retire to his bed, perhaps for days on end, until he had worked out in his mind every last detail of a solution.

For an account of the Duke's canal it is necessary to refer again to the pages of the earlier historian, Phillips, for who better than an employee of Brindley himself to explain the intricacies of canal works?

This stupendous canal was begun at a place called Worsley Mill, seven miles from Manchester, where, at the foot of a

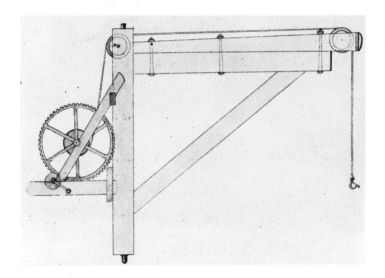

Left 'Side view of a Crane used at Stone Quarry for the Warwick & Napton Canal' – from *Utensils in Canal Work*
Below left Winding gear of a wharf crane
Below right Sluice-operating gear on the Grand Union Canal near Leicester
Opposite An unusual lock gate on the Stratford-upon-Avon Canal, near King's Norton; this 'stop lock' could compensate for differences in water levels on either side, from the days when each canal company was responsible for, and jealous of, its own water supply

A canal inn at Fradley Junction on the Trent and Mersey Canal

large mountain of coals, the Duke has cut a bason capable of containing many boats, and a great body of water, which is a reservoir and head to his navigation. At Barton bridge, three miles from the bason, begins an aqueduct, which, for upwards of 200 yards, conveys the canal across the river and along a valley, forty feet above the navigable river Irwell . . .

. . . But what is most ingenious, is the invention of floodgates that are under water and across the canal; they lie almost horizontally, a small matter inclining to each other, and at a quarter of a mile distance, in order that, if any part of it should break its banks, the draught of water rushing towards the breach may draw up the two floodgates, by which means no more water will be lost out of the canal than is between the two floodgates; and this, upon stopping the breach, is restored by letting the floodgates down again.

. . . The Duke's navigation is carried over the meadows on each side of the river Mersey; and quite across Sale-Moor, at incredible labour and expense. Mr Brindley caused trenches first to be made, and then placed deal balks in an upright position, from thirty to thirty-six feet long, backing and supporting them on the outside with other balks lengthways and in rows, and fastened together with screws, driving in some thousand of oak piles of different lengths, between them; and on the front side he threw the clay and the earth well rammed together to form his navigable canal. After finishing in this manner about forty yards, he proceeded again as before, in a line where it was intended the canal should continue.

An ingenious method was used to fill up the bed of the canal to a proper level. Two boats were fixed together within two feet of each other; between and over them was erected a

An early map showing the proposed
route of the Trent and Mersey Canal

trough large enough to contain eighteen tons of rubbish. The
bottom of this trough was composed of a line of doors or flaps;
which, upon drawing a pin, burst open and instantly dropped
the burthen. The usefulness of this contrivance is evident, for,
from a near spot, the trough was loaded, in a short time drawn
to the place wanted, and in an instant its contents deposited.

From the wharf . . . the poor of Manchester fetch their coals
in wheelbarrows, at three-pence halfpenny for a hundred weight
of seven score, which is not half the price they before paid for
that necessary article. But Mr Brindley, to remove the incon-
venience of carrying them up Castle Hill, has cut a large tunnel
through the centre of the hill, into which the barges are introduced; and by a crane that is worked by a box water-wheel of
thirty feet diameter, they are landed close to the town.

. . . The ingenuity and contrivance displayed through the
whole work is wonderful. The smiths' forges, the carpenters'
and masons' workshops were covered barges, which floated
on the canal, and followed the work as it went on, by which
means there was no hindrance of business, and as the Duke had
all the materials in his own possession, timber, stone, and lime
for mortar, and coals from his own estate all hard by, he has
been at little expense besides labour. It must be observed that
the Duke has made the refuse of one work serve for the construction of another; thus the stone that was dug up to make
the bason for the boats, at the foot of the mountain, as well as
others taken from out of the rock to make the tunnel, were
hewn into the proper forms to build bridges over rivers, brooks
and highways, and the piers and arches to support the aqueduct.
The clay, gravel, and earth taken up to preserve the level at

one place, are carried down the canal to raise the land in
another, or reserved to make bricks for other uses.

Here grandeur, elegance, and economy are happily united.
At first view it would seem that the work was intended to
excite astonishment. But on a closer inspection there is found
to be nothing unnecessary, and the whole has been finished at
an expense no way adequate to the undertaking; in short, the
work is truly admirable, and will be a standing monument of
public spirit and economy of the Duke of Bridgewater to the
end of time.

It is a sad stratagem of fate that great men are seldom
allowed to see the reality of their most cherished vision.
Telford's greatest canal work was not completed until after
his death, while Brunel's only journey over his unique
Tamar Bridge was made lying on his back in an open
truck while mortally sick. So, too, was James Brindley's
greatest ambition to remain for him unfulfilled.

The story of the canal from the Trent to the Mersey
began even before the Duke's project into Manchester.
Brindley was involved in these early proceedings and
remained at the helm of the venture for the rest of his life.
The canal is still known as the Trent and Mersey, but
Brindley's own name for it was the Grand Trunk, for he
saw it as a major coast-to-coast artery, its line forming a
wide 'V' across England, the two extended arms of which
pointed naturally to the other great ports of London and
Bristol. The cross-routes so formed would be the principal

Large teapot, Measham ware, of the pattern used and cherished by canal-boat families

highways of Brindley's future; other canals, like veins, would run from these arteries to permit a unifying interchange of trade and prosperity within. The geography of his vision has been realised in the present English canal system, but his pioneering enthusiasm seems long vanished.

The line of the Grand Trunk pushed south from its junction with the Duke of Bridgewater's Canal at Preston Brook; it passed through Brindley's first three main-line tunnels before reaching its summit and the barrier of Harecastle Hill. The tunnel through that hill, at $1\frac{3}{4}$ miles the longest known to have been constructed up to that time, took eleven years to complete and was not opened until five years after Brindley's death. It thus deprived him of his ambition to see the rivers Trent and Mersey united.

From Harecastle the cut was driven straight through the Potteries. Brindley here paid a debt to his old benefactors by providing them with a smooth road for the dispersal of their fragile goods and an efficient means of supply for large quantities of raw materials. The canal had its junction with the navigation of the Trent not at Burton, although this was the earliest convergence of both waterways, but at Wilden Ferry, fifteen miles to the east, thus avoiding the uncertainties of the river passage. One of Brindley's most frequently quoted opinions of rivers is that they were made to feed canals!

Of Brindley's other canal works the principal were the Staffordshire and Worcestershire Canal from Great Haywood, its junction with the Trent and Mersey, to his new

Summit Lock at Etruria, Trent and
Mersey Canal

An embankment slip at Rugeley during
the 1920s, Trent and Mersey Canal

Above Turnhurst Hall, Brindley's home near Kidsgrove—now demolished
Above right Brindley's burial place at Newchapel, near Kidsgrove

A page from one of Brindley's notebooks

town of Stourport on the River Severn, and the Coventry and Oxford canal routes which united Fradley on the Trent and Mersey with the Thames at Oxford. Thus were laid the foundations of water communication over inland routes between the four ports of Liverpool, Hull, Bristol and London.

James Brindley was 42 years of age when he first became involved with inland navigation. He died at 56. Within those fourteen years, as well as being engineer to the works already described, he superintended, surveyed, or was employed in some capacity, on other projects. These included the improvement of navigation of the Thames; a canal from Sonning to Richmond to by-pass the Thames; two plans for ship canals across the West Country, thus uniting the Bristol and English Channels; a canal through Stockton and Darlington; improvement of the Fen drains; the Forth and Clyde Canal; the Leeds and Liverpool Canal; and canals to serve Andover, Birmingham, Chester, Chesterfield, Derby, Droitwich, Lancaster, Salisbury and Selby. The list is probably far from complete. Brindley also successfully supervised the working of his Golden Hill mines during this period, and still found time for dreams. One such was for a canal between Runcorn and Liverpool which would have involved an aqueduct of more than a quarter of a mile in length across the Mersey estuary. Most fascinating, however, was his scheme for joining England to Ireland by a 'floating road and canal which would withstand the most violent attack of the waves'.

James Brindley died at his home on 27th September 1772. His resting-place is to be found today in a windswept, still poorly half-agrarian setting not far from the collapsed dream of Harecastle, and within sight of his Turnhurst estate. An electricity pylon now stands over the remains of his old hall. A heavy, almost permanent mist still hangs above the industry at Golden Hill, to darken a waste landscape of huge black sheds, chimneys, grey sterile fields and row upon row of brown terraced houses – the awful inverted consequence of this great engineer's work.

James Brindley was the first great English canal engineer. During his lifetime an agrarian country changed to an industrial nation. Mechanical invention, engineering knowledge, prosperity and poverty all increased with frightening rapidity. That evolution is still not concluded.

Many of the works left uncompleted by Brindley, including Harecastle Tunnel, were continued by his brother-in-law, Hugh Henshall, a one-time clerk of works on the Grand Trunk undertaking. Of the others, perhaps the most important was the trans-Pennine Leeds and Liverpool Canal which was to open a shorter, wider route between the two northern ports. Planned by Brindley, the project was carried to completion by his pupil, Robert Whitworth.

James Brindley's most notable successor in canal work was Thomas Telford. The first canal lines were often notoriously winding, not because the navigators were paid by the mile but because they followed natural contours and avoided heavy earth-moving works wherever possible.

Thomas Telford, 1757–1835, canal engineer

Telford and his contemporaries had more sophisticated techniques and more confident promoters; their lines were cut through hills and carried over valleys, while locks, where necessary, were concentrated into groups or 'flights' to make their working more efficient. Legend has it that the curvature of the earth was first measured accurately on a typically straight and level Telford canal.

Telford's birth and upbringing were in a district as rough

John Rennie, 1761–1821, canal engineer

Canals and their connections, now known as the Shropshire Union Canals. These form part of an alternative trunk route between Liverpool and Bristol, a route in which Brindley's canals have not been entirely superseded, for part of his Staffordshire and Worcestershire Canal is still the direct link from the Shropshire Union to the River Severn. Worthy of mention also, if only to show the extent of Telford's works, are his Caledonian Canal, providing a route for shipping through the Scottish lakes from east coast to west, and the Götha Canal, a similar large-scale project which he carried out in Sweden.

The third of the great builders of trunk canals was also a Scottish engineer. John Rennie was born at the farmstead of Phantassie, in East Lothian, in 1761. His apprenticeship was, like Brindley's, to a millwright. Without completing this he went on to obtain a classical education at the University of Edinburgh. This advanced learning was to show itself through the splendid classic designs of his later structures. As an engineer he is perhaps least known for his canals (his most famous design was that for the New London Bridge), but they are important here, particularly his Kennet and Avon Navigation, which provided the broad route between London and Bristol. Other canals under his direction were the Lancaster and Rochdale Canals, and the Royal Canal of Ireland.

The fourth side of the square of trunk routes is that from Hull to London, and these navigations are now known as the Grand Union Canals, which also connect with Bir-

as, and more isolated than, that of his famed predecessor; he was born a shepherd's son 'in one of the most solitary nooks of the narrow valley of the Esk' in the Scottish county of Dumfries, in 1757. He was to become in turn stonemason, surveyor, architect and engineer, famed as much for his roads and bridges as for his inland waterway work. Only the latter is of concern here.

Telford was responsible for the Ellesmere and Chester

A bollard worn by towing ropes

A parapet of an aqueduct near Kidsgrove on the Macclesfield Canal, showing the grooves worn by towing ropes

A half-mile plate, peculiar to the Brecon and Abergavenny Canal Company

A Grand Junction Canal Company mile-plate

GJCCo
LEICESTER
39
MILES

SHROPSHIRE UNION RAILWAY
AND CANAL COMPANY
NOTICE
THIS BRIDGE IS INSUFFICIENT TO CARRY
WEIGHTS BEYOND THE ORDINARY
TRAFFIC OF THE DISTRICT BY ORDER

Navigation Office in Birmingham in the early nineteenth century

Paddle gear beside a derelict maintenance depot on the Oxford Canal

The entrance to the Basingstoke Canal near
Byfleet
Right Gas works by the Regent's Canal in the
early nineteenth century

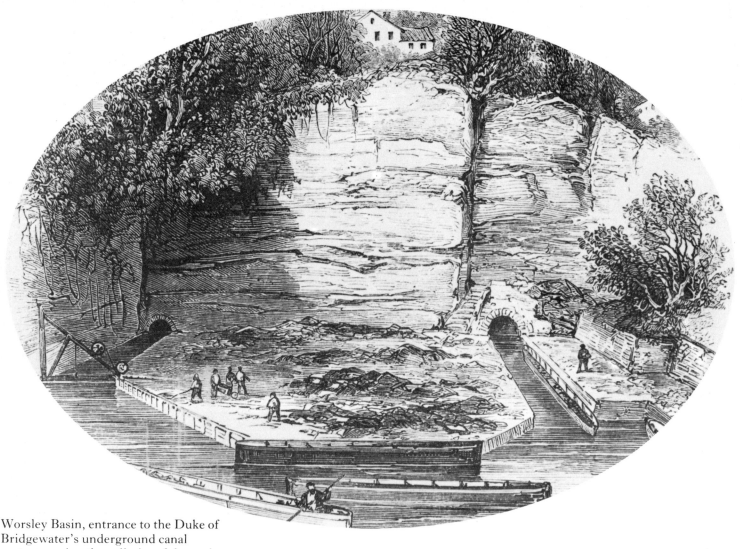

Worsley Basin, entrance to the Duke of Bridgewater's underground canal system serving the galleries of the coal-mines

mingham. Many engineers were involved on these lines, principal among them being James Barnes and William Jessop, while others included Whitworth, Rennie, and Benjamin Outram.

Of the awesome problems overcome and the great works executed by all these engineers more will be found in the following pages. The present chapter may best be concluded by returning to the historian Smiles and his description of the beginnings of the English canal system:

Worsley-basin lies at the base of a cliff of sandstone, some hundred feet in height. Luxuriant foliage overhangs its pre-cipitous side, and beyond is seen the graceful spire of Worsley church. In contrast to this bright nature above, lies the almost stagnant pool beneath. The barges are deeply laden with their black freight, which they have brought from the mine through the two low, semi-circular arches opening at the base of the rock, such being the entrances to the underground canals, which now extend to nearly forty miles in all directions. Where the tunnel passed through earth or coal, the arching was of brick-work; but where it passed through rock, it was simply hewn out. This tunnel acts not only as a drain and water-feeder for the canal itself, but as a means of carrying the facilities of the navigation through the very heart of the collieries.

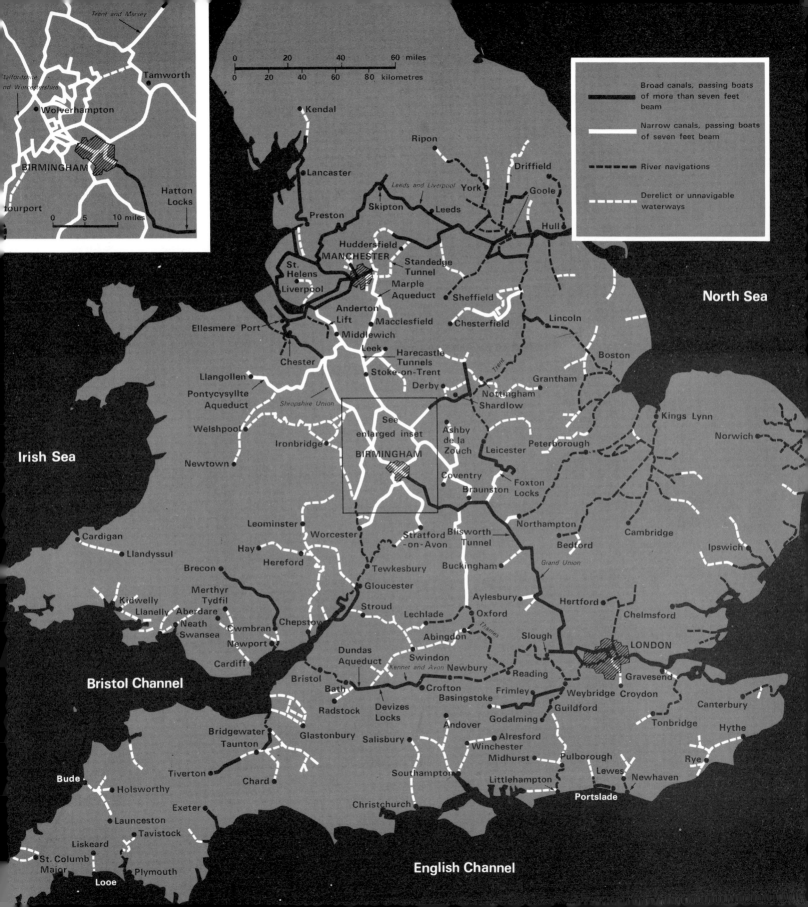

Inset (top left):

Trent and Mersey

Staffordshire and Worcestershire

Tamworth

Wolverhampton

BIRMINGHAM

Hatton Locks

...ourport

0 5 10 miles

Scale (top):

0 20 40 60 miles

0 20 40 60 80 kilometres

Legend:

Broad canals, passing boats of more than seven feet beam

Narrow canals, passing boats of seven feet beam

River navigations

Derelict or unnavigable waterways

Map labels:

North Sea

Irish Sea

Bristol Channel

English Channel

Kendal

Ripon

Lancaster

Driffield

York

Goole

Leeds and Liverpool

Skipton

Leeds

Hull

Preston

Huddersfield

MANCHESTER

Standedge Tunnel

St. Helens

Marple Aqueduct

Liverpool

Sheffield

Anderton Lift

Macclesfield

Chesterfield

Lincoln

Ellesmere Port

Middlewich

Boston

Leek

Chester

Harecastle Tunnels

Stoke-on-Trent

Grantham

Llangollen

Derby

Nottingham

Trent

Pontycysyllte Aqueduct

Shardlow

Shropshire Union

Kings Lynn

Welshpool

Ashby de la Zouch

Leicester

Peterborough

Norwich

Ironbridge

See enlarged inset

Newtown

BIRMINGHAM

Coventry

Foxton Locks

Braunston

Cambridge

Leominster

Northampton

Ipswich

Worcester

Stratford-on-Avon

Blisworth Tunnel

Cardigan

Bedford

Llandyssul

Hay

Hereford

Buckingham

Grand Union

Brecon

Tewkesbury

Merthyr Tydfil

Gloucester

Hertford

Kidwelly

Aberdare

Chelmsford

Llanelly

Neath

Stroud

Lechlade

Oxford

Swansea

Cwmbran

Chepstow

Aylesbury

Newport

Abingdon

Slough

LONDON

Cardiff

Dundas Aqueduct

Swindon

Reading

Gravesend

Bristol

Kennet and Avon

Newbury

Weybridge

Croydon

Bath

Crofton

Basingstoke

Frimley

Guildford

Canterbury

Radstock

Devizes Locks

Godalming

Tonbridge

Hythe

Bridgewater

Andover

Alresford

Pulborough

Taunton

Glastonbury

Salisbury

Winchester

Midhurst

Lewes

Rye

Tiverton

Chard

Southampton

Littlehampton

Newhaven

Bude

Christchurch

Portslade

Holsworthy

Exeter

Launceston

Tavistock

Liskeard

St. Columb Major

Plymouth

Looe

BASINGSTOKE
CANAL
NAVIGATION.

TAKE NOTICE,

That all Persons Trespassing on these PLANTATIONS under any pretence whatever, or committing *Damage, Injury, or Spoil thereon, will be* forthwith prosecuted.

By Order of the Company of Proprietors of the Basingstoke Canal Navigation.

CHARLES HEADEACH,

Clerk to the Company.

Basingstoke, 1st October, 1858.

R. Cottle, Printer, Basingstoke.

BRIDGES AND IRON

Two men whose lives were contemporaneous with the founding of the Canal Age were William Edwards of Glamórganshire and John Wilkinson of Cumberland. Although having backgrounds and characters entirely dissimilar, both may be given the distinction of having revived the art of bridge-building in Britain.

William Edwards had started his working life as a labourer on his mother's small farm in the parish of Eglwysilian. Through self-education and patient observation of the mason's skill, he built up for himself within only a few years such a reputation in this craft that any local construction project of unusual magnitude or difficulty was inevitably directed to him. Thus it was that, in 1746, he was employed to build a new bridge over the River Taff at Pont-y-Prydd. He produced a satisfactory structure of three arches, but failed to consider nature's forces, for after only two and a half years a heavy flood brought down such a mass of debris against its piers that the bridge was swept away.

Determined that such an occurrence should not be repeated, Edwards' second attempted design consisted of only one arch, spanning 140 feet. This was a daring undertaking, as the greatest span known to have been erected previously, at least since Roman times, was of 100 feet. The forces of the new bridge, however, were proved to be without equilibrium when even before completion its components ended up on the river bottom.

The third bridge was again single-arched, its span being

William Edwards, 1719–1789, who revolutionised bridge-building in Britain

The bridge at Pont-y-Pridd, built in 1755

a segment of a circle of 170 feet in diameter. Here the haunches were lightened by piercing each one with three cylindrical holes of nine, six and three feet diameters. This expedient was by no means new, but the way in which Edwards used his roundels suggests that the idea was his own, the product of bitter experience rather than known precedent. Completed in 1755, the 'rainbow bridge' stands today as faithful testimony to the effectiveness of its construction.

John Wilkinson was the first, and perhaps the greatest ironmaster. He was well known for his seemingly preposterous forecasts that the time would come when 'we should live in houses of iron and even navigate the seas in ships of iron'. So 'iron-mad' was he that he had cast a coffin of the material for his own burial.

When he pronounced that the projected new bridge

The Iron Bridge at Coalbrookdale

over the Severn at Coalbrookdale should be of iron, such was his reputation and influence that the bridge company was obliged to offer some consideration to the apparently absurd suggestion. The opinion was taken of Mr Pritchard, an architect of Shrewsbury, who approved of the use of iron and provided a design for a single span of 100 feet. To allow for the passage beneath of high masted trows and other Severn craft, the arch was a semi-circle. The roadway was supported on great ribs, each being cast in two pieces. The work was carried out under contract by Reynold and Darby, ironmasters of Coalbrookdale. The bridge was completed in 1779, and the weight of iron used was 378 tons.

Here were two landmarks of British bridge-building just prior to the Canal Age: Pont-y-Prydd, forcing a well-tried material into hitherto unimagined forms, and Iron-bridge (Coalbrookdale), heralding a new era of invention and engineering. The initial effect these advances were to have on the numerous structures which gave accommodation to tracks, paths and highways across the artificial waterways of Britain was apparently slight. Their introduction was to make its impression in other branches of canal engineering. Thus the roundels were equally functional only in Benjamin Outram's great aqueduct at Marple, although many tunnel portals continued their form as inherent features of decoration, most notably at Sapperton on the Thames and Severn Canal, and at Greywell on the Basingstoke Canal. Iron, of course, is present in all canal machinery and in most canal structures, but its bridge forms are most apparent in aqueducts great and small, carrying the water-channel of the canal itself within their spans.

Above A bridge on the Trent and Mersey Canal
Below Scotland Bridge on the Basingstoke Canal, near Woking

A stone bridge near Brecon, on the Brecon & Abergavenny Canal

The worthy achievements of Pont-y-Prydd and Ironbridge little influenced the first canal bridges for there were no great distances to be spanned and no currents to be resisted. Seven feet of waterway, three feet of towpath, and the height of a horse, were the required limits of the passage beneath. Construction was no more advanced than that needed to carry a turnpike over a stream. Early bridges, often the work of local masons, were profound in their informal simplicity, the best examples of a functional tradition whose motives are today so highly regarded. What is most admired, perhaps, is their honesty shown by a total lack of conscious design or decoration. Modern parallels may be the motorway bridges which at best are simply structural statements of reinforced concrete arousing little comment and seldom being derided or admired. They will remain largely unnoticed until their inherent usefulness is lost or superseded, when their passing may well be mourned.

Many of these early canal bridges were built only to afford communication between the fields and land which the newly cut canal divided, and where this land has remained agricultural, so the bridges have remained. The bridges built for wagons, however, have not withstood the onslaught of heavy motor traffic, and the hump-back canal bridge is disappearing from British roads.

Accommodation bridges between fields were not always constructed in the hump-back style. Passages over them were invariably light or infrequent – cows passing to and

Left A bridge on the southern line of the Grand Union Canal
Below A stone bridge on the Brecon and Abergavenny Canal, approaching Brecon

from the milking parlour, perhaps – and thus the expense of a brick structure with ramped approaches was not seen to be justified. The cheapest bridge form which could fulfil the purpose often consisted of a platform set very nearly level with the canal, and capable of being moved sideways or upwards to leave the channel clear. Such movable bridges were obvious choices where the waterway lay on the surface of the land through which it passed (nearly always the case with the earlier 'contour' canals), but considerable savings were also made by not having to span across a towpath. The time involved in operating these bridges was of no consequence to the boatmen, for their land use was so limited that they were left open to canal traffic, and the pedestrian was left to face the problem of negotiating a bridge closed against him on the opposite bank of the canal – a problem presumably overcome with the help of one of the frequently passing boats. Today, with the decline in water-borne traffic, the position is reversed and on the more heavily used canal routes such bridges, once numerous, have largely been eliminated.

Most common of these movable bridges are the drawbridges, where the platform lifts to a near vertical plane, leaving the channel entirely clear. The type designed by Brindley on the Oxford Canal is the simplest and possibly the most pleasing of these. The platform is counterbalanced by projecting fixed beams which, when the bridge is open, lie in a horizontal plane and, when it is closed, rise accordingly. The platform itself is often in the form of a shallow

A lifting-bridge on the Prees
branch of the Welsh Canal

Iron bridge in Birmingham

arch, but sometimes it is flat. Handrails are mounted either side. The construction, apart from hinges and retaining bands of iron, is of timber. The water channel is closed to a width of seven feet at the point of crossing to reduce the weight and cost of the structure.

The alternative form of drawbridge is found most frequently on the Welsh canals. Its design has its origin in the Netherlands although it was used, in primitive form, at British harbour entrances in medieval times. The platform is again hinged on the bank opposite to the towpath, and has chains at its lifting end attached to an overhead frame. This frame is pivoted on a static mounting, also on the bank side, extending behind the platform to give balance and to act as a lever. The force is applied by pulling down a chain on the balance end of the frame, which lifts the front end and the attached platform. On the Welsh bridges a box is carried across the balanced end of the frames to which extra weights may be added, thus compensating for changes in the weights of the platforms due to repair and renovation. In one case, where the bridge has been considerably strengthened to allow the passage of heavy road traffic to an adjacent mill, the frame is pulled down by a winch.

This type of drawbridge has the advantage over those on the Oxford Canal of being stronger, but the overhead frame limits the height of vehicles able to use it. Besides the Welsh canals examples may still be found elsewhere, as on the Caldon Branch of the Trent and Mersey Canal.

Vertically-rising lifting-bridge carrying a horse-wagon way over Preston Basin, Lancaster in 1897

Probably there were many more drawbridges than those of which evidence can now be seen, but the disadvantages of continued maintenance to moving parts and renewal of defective timbers led to their early replacement. It is known that several were erected on the long defunct Salisbury and Southampton Canal, but none now remain in southern England.

The alternative form of moving bridge is the swing- or turnbridge. Here the platform is pivoted on the bank side and moves horizontally into a recess, again leaving the channel entirely clear. More expensive to construct than drawbridges, and more difficult to maintain, they were nevertheless still cheaper than fixed bridges on wide canals, and were extensively used. Many still remain and worthy of note are those on the Kennet and Avon Canal, some of which carry quite heavy modern traffic while remaining easy to swing. This is unusual because the tendency is for the steel and timber platforms to break their backs or wear out the pivot bearings so that they rest firmly, and in some cases almost immovably, on the banks. A number of these bridges were also used on the western end of the Basingstoke Canal before that section became derelict, but none has survived. A swing-bridge, large or small, road or foot, can be found here and there on nearly all canals and branches but they still occur most frequently on the Grand Union, Peak Forest and Macclesfield Canals.

The choice between swinging or lifting bridges was determined by the dimensions of the canal. To counter-

Mechanical drawbridge above Longcot Top Lock on the now defunct Wiltshire and Berkshire Canal in 1895

The pivoting platform of a typical Grand Union Canal swing-bridge

balance a lifting platform over a fourteen-foot span would have been uneconomical, therefore drawbridges are most frequently found on narrow waterways (some, on the canals of South Wales, passed boats of 9 feet 2 inches in beam). The subject of moving bridges would not be complete without some mention of the very rare rolling- or sliding-bridge. Thomas Telford designed a very fine example for his Götha Canal in Sweden. Confusingly, spans with this movement are also often termed drawbridges because the platform is drawn back on itself to clear the channel.

With the 'railway age' came sophistication in the designs of mechanical moving bridges over large navigations, the results of which are best studied on the River Weaver and Manchester Ship Canal, both engineered by E Leader Williams. The working of these giant bridges calls for resident operators in all cases.

In addition to such bridges giving passage over the canal to other transport forms, navigation of the canal itself is dependent on the towpath-bridge and the lock bridge. The towpath was provided on whichever side of the channel would most conveniently accommodate it, depending on the situations of land-ownership and on engineering works. For example, a farmer might have a right to water cattle from a navigation, in which case the towpath would be best made on the bank opposite his land. As the situations varied with the areas through which the waterway was to pass, so the towpath crossed from side to side, and hence

there was a need to transfer the towing animal with it. On some river navigations the only means of so doing was by boats kept for the purpose at such points. This was the case well into the present century on the Upper Thames, where the horse-ferries were owned and operated by the Navigation Authority. In the Bedford Levels gangs of lighters would take a small horse-boat in tow with them for the purpose. On the Trent, the carrying vessel itself would be used to ferry its horses. On canals, a bridge was always used and often the siting of it was chosen so that it could double as an accommodation bridge. Some of these, called 'towpath roving' bridges, were merely single spans carrying no towpath through them. To pass such a bridge the towing line was disconnected and the animal led over while the vessel continued under its own momentum through the arch. Such a situation often occurred, even on 'overline' bridges on river navigations, when, if proceeding upstream, the boat had to 'hold to' and wait for the towing line to be floated down to it from above the bridge. The towpath bridges of the Macclesfield and Peak Forest routes are elegant in their simplicity. The towpath is first carried under the arch then turned over itself to gain the other bank, thus avoiding any unhitching of the towrope. These are termed 'turnover' bridges, and are classic examples of canal functionalism. On the Stratford-upon-Avon Canal the same problem is overcome without the expense of spanning across the towpath. The bridge platform is constructed in two pieces, each cantilevered

A swing-bridge over the River Weaver

A timber rolling-bridge designed by Telford for use on his Götha Canal

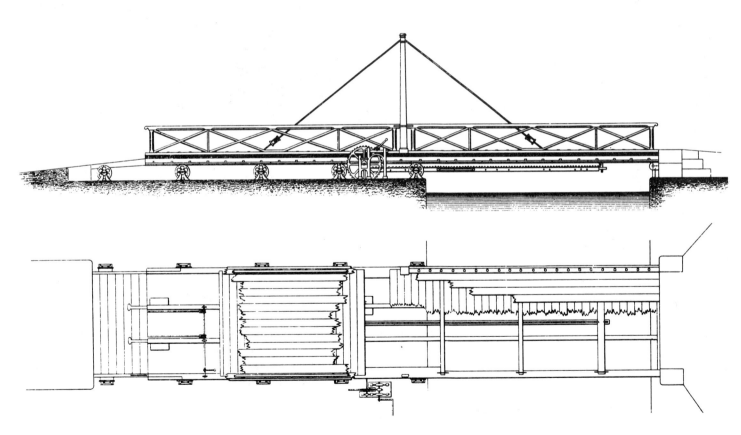

Above Functional simplicity expressed in a turnover bridge at Marple, the junction of the Macclesfield and Peak Forest Canals

Left A roving bridge carrying the path of the main line of the Welsh Canal over the branch leading to Ellesmere Basin

Opposite A roving bridge of cast iron with a central slot to allow the towrope to be passed through, at Kingswood on the Stratford-upon-Avon Canal

A sophisticated lock bridge at Watford Locks, on the Leicester Section of the Grand Union Canal

Simplicity at Foxton Locks, on the Leicester Section of the Grand Union Canal

from its buttress toward the other, but leaving a gap of about one inch. Through this gap is passed the towing line. The cantilevers are of iron, with integral hand rails. Many years of neglect have caused most bridges of this type to fall together, some having reinforcing bars across the span, thus rendering them unable to carry out their first intended purpose. Towpath bridges also occur at canal junctions where the paths of each navigation must connect. The best example of such a junction bridge is to be found at Marple, where traffic can pass unhindered between three canals, the Macclesfield, Upper Peak Forest and Lower Peak Forest.

The purpose of lock bridges (built always over the lower ends to avoid raised approaches) is to enable the locks to be more easily worked. On the narrow Shropshire Union and Welsh canals they are not provided, for the locks do not have a great fall and are worked by platforms built on to each gate. This practice was also carried out on the earlier Trent and Mersey, and Staffordshire and Worcestershire canals, but, because the fall was greater (eleven feet was usual, compared with seven feet on the Shropshire Union), the operation was physically and psychologically more precarious and thus footbridges were often provided. On these latter waterways they were brick-arched exten-

sions of the lock chamber. For the boatmen passing up the canal these arches were a nuisance, preventing a tow right into the chamber. Coming down was simpler because a flush of water from the upper pound would sufficiently move the boat out of the lock so that the line could be dropped and attached from above. Fortunately this type of lock bridge is only found where it doubles as an overline bridge, or where substantial access is, or was, required to a lock-side house.

Elsewhere can be found less ambitious but equally effective cantilever lock bridges, as those on the Stratford-upon-Avon Canal. In some cases these are merely iron brackets set in the chamber sides with a path of timber planking on them. On the Staffordshire and Worcestershire Canal some examples still remain of all-iron footbridges of this type, none of which is now usable. Although these date from the time of construction of the canal there are many on other canals which were added later, when their value was realised.

A curious variation is the single cantilever lock bridge found only on the Worcester and Birmingham Canal. Here the bridge is a wooden platform, usually with handrails, heavily weighted or set in concrete on the bank side so that

Above Aston Lock, a cantilever
lock bridge on the Trent and
Mersey Canal
Above right Another canti-
lever lock bridge on the
Trent and Mersey Canal

Single cantilever bridge over
Lock 33 on the Worcester
and Birmingham Canal

Decorative bridge in Cassiobury Park, Watford

the other end is raised two or three inches off the ground allowing the towing line to pass through the gap. Only one of these is in its original condition. Because of the structural limitations, cantilever bridges are only to be found on narrow canals. Wide locks are sometimes spanned with narrow footways of iron, timber, or more recently, concrete.

There are many instances of ornamental and heavily decorated bridges throughout the canal system. These were provided, principally, where the canal passed through a manorial estate, and it was required that the waterway and its encumbrances should be of an appropriate quality. Alternatively the canal might have been incorporated in a formal garden or park layout, such as the one at Cassiobury Park, Watford. Sometimes there is no apparent reason for their occurrence, except perhaps to show off the skill of the local mason. It may be conjectured that some were erected as monuments to local heroes, long forgotten.

Notable both for its appearance and its history is Macclesfield Bridge, c.1829, which crosses the Regent's Canal to the north of Regent's Park. *The Mirror of Literature, Amusement and Instruction* of 10th January 1829 described it thus: 'Its piers are formed by cast-iron columns of the Grecian Doric order, from which spring the arches, covering the towingpath, the canal itself, and the southern bank.' The architect was a Mr Elmes, who said of it, a little immodestly, 'it is scarcely surpassed for lightness, elegance and originality by any in Europe'.

The bridge did not achieve any great notoriety until 2nd October 1874, when, at about five o'clock in the morning, *Tilbury*, last in tow of a train of five barges, passed under it. The cargo included five tons of gunpowder. A contemporary report in the *Illustrated London News* related as follows:

The *Tilbury* was directly under the bridge when by some means yet unexplained, the powder caught fire and the whole was blown up. The men on board this barge were killed, and

Macclesfield Bridge on the Regent's Canal, before the explosion

'Scene of the explosion on the Regent's Canal' – the blowing-up of the Macclesfield Bridge

the barge was shattered to pieces, while one of the other barges was sunk. A column of thick smoke and a great blaze of fire followed the explosion. The bridge was entirely destroyed; several of the neighbouring houses were half-ruined, their roofs and walls being greatly injured; and in hundreds of other houses, a mile east or west of the place, the windows were broken, and many fragile articles of furniture. . . . The noise and shock were perceived in every quarter of London, and in many instances ten or twelve miles away, both on the north and on the south side of the Thames . . .

In spite of this rapid dispersal of its components the bridge was rebuilt and stands today just as it was when first erected. The 'cast-iron columns of the Grecian Doric order', however, were replaced incorrectly, for the grooves cut into them after many years of horse-towing now face away from the canal.

Canal spans were not at first great enough to justify the expense of using iron, especially where brick and masonry

56

Above Telford's magnificent iron bridge at Galton, over the Birmingham Canal, with a span of 150 feet and a height of 75 feet

Left and far left A horse-tunnel at the 'Sixteen Locks', Marple, on the Peak Forest Canal

were available locally. In areas badly affected by mining subsidence it quickly became apparent that continual rebuilding of brick bridges affected by earth movement was unnecessarily costly, for a platform supported on iron girders was easy to jack up under such circumstances.

Iron canal bridges sometimes exploited the spanning properties of that metal. In 1826 a 'magnificent bridge' was erected over the new line of the Birmingham Canal at Smethwick, four miles from Birmingham. 'The original canal, which communicated with the collieries, was inconveniently narrow, and very winding in its course. These defects have been remedied by opening a new line of canal executed under the directions of the late Mr Telford, which, by wide and deep cuttings, avoids the necessity of the ascending and descending chain of locks, which impede the former communication. This canal is also remarkable for the grand proportions of the bridges of masonry and iron, which cross the deep excavations. Of these structures, the Galton Bridge is a superb specimen. It was cast at the

Towpath bridge at Great Haywood, junction of the Trent and Mersey and Staffordshire and Worcestershire Canals

Left High Bridge, over a Telford cutting on the Shropshire Union Canal

Opposite Iron foot-bridge cast at Horseley Iron Works

UPPER BRATCH

Nº 48

BRIDGE

Horseley Iron Works, from a design by Mr Telford.' (*The Mirror of Literature, Amusement and Instruction,* 15th April 1837.)

There are many elegant iron spans to be seen on British canals today, often with the legend 'Horseley Iron Works' cast into the structure. When Telford straightened out Brindley's original wanderings of the Oxford Canal, many parts of the old line were retained as branches to serve villages and local manufactories. The new towpath was carried over these branches by bridges from Horseley, many of which still exist as graceful companions to the earlier arches of brick.

Similarly, on the Birmingham canals, as more and more branches were opened to serve factories and timber yards, so continuity of the towpath was assured by bridges of brick and iron. Many have now taken on a sombre and ominous quality as they cling close to massive faceless warehouses or bleakly span only vacant blackness.

Study in stone and iron at Camden, on the Regent's Canal

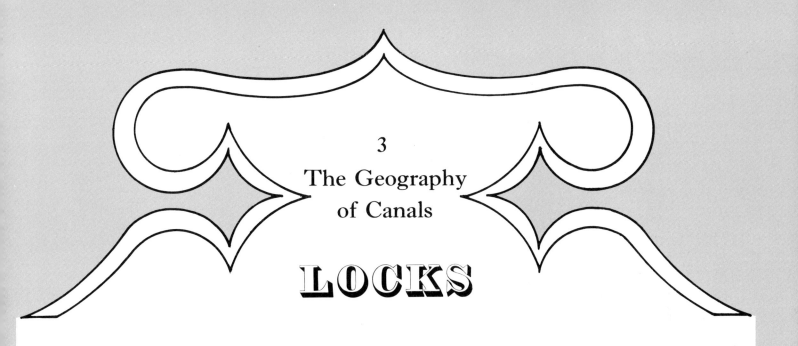

3

The Geography of Canals

LOCKS

The extensive inland navigation system of the Netherlands is perfectly suited to its terrain; the low-lying land is quite flat, and considerable lengths of canal can be cut easily without having to overcome any great rise or fall. Tidal rivers, also, flow much further inland, dividing it, draining it, and providing arterial transport routes from coastal ports. Few lands can claim such an ideal condition for the cutting of artificial channels to link and shorten these natural routes.

In England, trade routes were needed which would connect areas producing raw materials to manufacturing towns (these were usually situated on rivers, being dependent on the water power) and from these towns to the main ports. The most important of such routes would be those going from east coast to west coast, and from north to south. Thus would Liverpool, Bristol and London be connected by trunks serving producing and manufacturing districts. Such undertakings could not be carried through without penetrating great dividing ridges such as the north-south Pennine range, the southern Marlborough and Berkshire Downs, and the Chiltern Hills. Rises of several hundreds of feet were involved.

It might justifiably be said that water, which must lie level, was a most unsuitable medium from which to form these undulating courses. However, it has always been the most capable of carrying the greatest loads, and it was up to the engineers to answer the problems arising from level changes, both by physically overcoming them and in

Left The machinery of the lock

Victorian scene on the Thames, Sonning Lock

finding water for high canal reaches, yet still to maintain the advantages of inland waterways as efficient transport routes.

A river that was wide enough to be easily navigable did not usually present any definite changes in level. Shallows, however, were a problem. One reason for the large number of men required to haul a boat up the Severn, in England, against the stream (from 50 to 90 was said to be the average number) was that for a great deal of the time the boat was being dragged with its keel in contact with the river bed. Where the silting was particularly serious and the boat completely grounded, an obstruction would be thrown across the channel downstream of the boat, thus building up a great enough head of water to refloat the vessel. This head of water was called a 'flash', and could be achieved in several ways. Most effective but least sensible

was a barrier of rocks and earth which could only add to the obstruction of the navigation. The procedure most often followed was for some of the hauliers themselves to wade in and form a human dam, or, if a herd of cattle was conveniently close by, it would be driven in to form a 'cow flash'. Such methods met the minimal needs of river navigation through its earliest period, but the demands for water gradually began to extend beyond transport needs.

The small coastal communities which relied on sea-fishing for their living had not the means to communicate or trade regularly with the farmers very far inland; it was to fresh water that the latter looked for a supplement to their diet. Fish weirs were laid across the rivers to provide catchment areas and larger breeding grounds; they also provided effective obstructions to navigation.

Such obstruction was not so serious as that imposed by

the miller, who during the Middle Ages was becoming more and more aware of the value of a large impounded head of water to power his wheels. All these demands could not be harmoniously met, and many were the bitter disputes as to whose was the greatest right, each merchant being of seemingly equal worth to the inland community. Each faction needed the head of water; the fish-farmer and the miller, however, would hold it up permanently and prevent all navigation. Furthermore, a large head could only create further severe shallows below it.

The navigators were fortunate, in some cases, to have one influential patron: on many rivers free passage of vessels was a right granted by the sovereign. Weirs on such waters were provided with a removable section, consisting usually of planks dropped into slots or held against stanchions by water pressure, and these planks were removed to allow a passage. It can be imagined that the operation of this apparatus was hazardous. Time and water were not to be wasted by the anxious miller, and the boat travelling

downstream was forced to 'ride' the running flash over the shallows, while pulling against such a voluminous stream was a gargantuan task. The boat would often need to be unloaded in such a case so that the hauliers would have to move only its own weight.

Eventually every community had at least one mill, so that any single river was considerably obstructed, the normal flow was restricted, and a flash released for the passage of a vessel took some time to build up again. In order that the miller would not be continually held up by this he very often had the counter-right to stipulate when the flash could be released. Needless to say, the rights were abused by both sides, leading to even fiercer disputes. No greater evidence is necessary to show the importance of river navigation than that it continued to increase through all such adversity.

If the navigable weir, or its antecedent the 'flash lock', where the planks are replaced by a counterbalanced gate and sometimes provided with a winch to open it against

Operating a lock beneath the Gawksholme Viaduct carrying the
Manchester and Leeds Railway over the Rochdale Canal. A
lithograph by A. F. Tait, dated 1845

An engraving of 1793, after J. Farington, showing the Thames
& Severn Canal at its junction with the Thames at Inglesham,
Gloucestershire. The circular lock house of Cotswold stone,
typical of those built on this waterway, survives although the
canal is derelict

Turfpole Staunch, a 'flash lock' on the
Brandon River in 1897

'Opening a Lock'
from *Life on the Upper Thames*,
1875

An early Thames lock at
Abingdon

A Thames and Severn Canal Token,
struck to commemorate the opening of
the canal in 1795

a heavy stream, is seen to be so inefficient, it is incredible to record that some examples remained in existence well into the present century. Examples in the Fen districts of England, known as 'staunches', had vertically rising gates, and the overhead lifting gear, consisting of rollers turned by huge spoked wheels, must have presented weird interruptions to the ever flat terrain.

Flash locks hindered no less a navigation than the River Thames until the present century. Even after the Thames and Severn Canal had opened up an apparently reasonable water route between London and Bristol, the section from Oxford to Lechlade required the passage of many of these devices. Their presence certainly contributed to the failure of the canal; railway competition caused steady deterioration towards the end of the nineteenth century, and all attempts at restoration proved abortive. The last boat passed beneath the Cotswolds through the 2-mile-long Sapperton Tunnel in 1911.

A century after its conception (supposedly by Leonardo da Vinci), the 'pound lock' found its way into Britain. Like its continental forbear, the British example, built on John Trew's Exeter Canal of 1566, had lifting gates. The machine consisted, in fact, of two Fen-type staunches placed close together, the 'pound' so formed between them being of sufficient length to contain only one of the boats normally using the canal.

Pound locks built shortly afterwards on the Thames were enclosed by now conventional swinging gates. The River Wey in Surrey was made navigable from the Thames to Guilford under an Act of 1651, and was provided with pound locks, some of which have survived almost in their original 'turf-sided' state until the present day. Piling is needed to keep vessels roughly central while working through, but the chief disadvantage of this early form of construction is excessive water consumption by the porous sides.

The canal lock has evolved with a chamber of masonry, iron, or latterly concrete and steel. Generally rectangular in plan, this chamber is designed to store and consume the smallest possible amount of water while allowing passage of the largest type of craft on the canal. The 'narrow' chamber of the Trent and Mersey and connecting Midland canals has a width of 7 feet at the top, and a length of about 76 feet, being designed around boats 6 feet 10 inches in beam and from 70 to 72 feet in length, the extra chamber length allowing for the inward-opening bottom gates.

A vertically-rising lock-gate at King's
Norton on the Stratford-upon-Avon Canal

Iron chambered lock, Beeston, on the
Shropshire Union Canal

The chamber side is not vertical: it is a retaining wall, battered outwards to top and centre. In spite of this, and especially where the walls are of brick, earth pressure has in times past forced them together, with the rather dramatic consequence of boats working down being literally 'hung up' in the lock.

The machinery of the lock is as simple in principle and action as the appliance itself. The sequence of operation of a pound lock is to equate water levels in lock and stretch being passed from, contain the vessel in the lock, and equate its level with the stretch being passed into.

Gates of timber are, like most canal works, self-maintaining when kept in use. The seals of the gate planking itself, and between gates and lock sides, are most efficient through continual immersion. Lack of this property is a serious disadvantage in gates of any other material. Iron gates were used on the Montgomeryshire and Ellesmere Canals early in the nineteenth century, a pair from the former being exhibited at the Waterways Museum, Stoke Bruerne, but no better answer was found in either case than to have timber inserts at the heads to complete the seal.

The life span of a timber gate is relative to its use; the chief enemy, perhaps, is ice. Such gates can last from 50 to even 100 years, but there is little danger that the crafts of building and fitting them will yet die out for there are some 2000 locks still in operation on the system, most with gates of timber. Mass-production is unthought of in the maintenance yards, for there is hardly a navigation which can claim

A turf-sided lock at Papercourt on the
River Wey under reconstruction in 1968

Simplest and earliest form of paddle gear, still in use on the River Wey

Enclosed paddle gear on the Trent and Mersey Canal

Above Paddle gear in the Canal Basin, Stourport. The initials B.C.N. are those of the Birmingham Canal Navigations, although in fact Stourport is on the Staffordshire and Worcestershire Canal
Right Paddle gear at the 'Sixteen Locks', Peak Forest Canal

Above left Paddle gear on
the Welsh Canal at
Grindley Brook
Above right Typical
River Weaver paddle gear

Partially-enclosed paddle
gear on the Oxford Canal,
near Napton

71

Elements of the canal lock

Single narrow boat working through a lock at Middlewich, Trent and Mersey Canal

complete dimensional uniformity of its lock equipment. For this same reason steel gates, which have been used with success, will never become an economical proposition without widespread modification of chambers.

To adjust the water level of a lock, sluices are fitted at each end. At the top, ground sluices are common, the side of the reach being connected to the side of the chamber by a bore of about two feet in diameter. Gate sluices alone would be unsatisfactory, for if fully opened the resulting jets of water would cascade into the bows of any boat hard up against the apron. Gate sluices are invariably fitted only at the bottom.

Sluices are regulated by means of timber shutters with fixed handles by which they may be raised or lowered vertically. Because of their shape they are known as 'paddles' and are seated in grooves against the higher water level, the pressure, again, aiding the seals.

On the River Wey some paddles still operate in their most primitive form, lifted by hand and positioned by pegs through regular holes in the flat handles. Most commonly, paddles are raised by a form of rack and pinion gearing, the pinion axle being turned by a detachable crank ('windlass' or 'lock key') carried by the operator. Other types still extant use a wooden handspike to raise the vertical rack.

The operation of a narrow lock by a working boatman can be spectacularly swift. Arriving at the bottom of one which is full, he places his bows at the apex of the bottom gates and leaves the engine idling in forward gear. He swiftly winds all bottom paddles, the lock empties, and his now uncontrolled vessel pushes open the gates and comes to rest against a rubbing board in front of the apron. By this time the boatman has a top paddle raised, and the channelled surge slams shut the bottom gates. The chamber fills, and the boat begins to propel itself out, leaving its master just time to drop all paddles before taking stance once more at his tiller. Locking down is more tedious, although here again the professional has his techniques—

Pleasure and commercial traffic on the Leicester line. The boat on the right, the *Tay,* was originally a Thomas Clayton tar boat, designed to carry liquid cargoes
Below The inclined plane at Ketley—a commemorative canal token

for instance, the use of his check strap over the 'strapping post' (an extension of the head post) of the top gate on entering, both to close it and to brake the forward momentum of his vessel.

To change level in a narrow lock with a fall of seven feet involves a transference of about 20,000 gallons of water from the reach above the lock to that below it. The hydraulics of lock operation requires a lengthy study of its own, written preferably by a mathematician and with the aid of a computer. Basic principles, however, are that the least amount of water is lost from the upper reach when an unladen light vessel locks up, or when a fully laden heavy vessel occupying the entire chamber area locks down. Also, the most economical sequence of traffic flow is for vessels to pass alternately up and down through a lock, one lockful of water thereby working for two vessels, a procedure which is enforced during times of serious drought although, unavoidably, it leads to considerable delay. At the design stage, however, the worst case must

be allowed for. Thus the water supply to the summit level of any canal has to be sufficient to pass the whole expected volume of traffic over it, going theoretically in one direction only.

Reservoirs, because they involve the permanent requisition of large areas of land both for catchment and for storage, are most expensive features of canal construction. Canal proprietors have, therefore, constantly been pressured by engineers, inventors and even journalists to employ varying schemes for building waterways able to traverse undulating terrains but without the disadvantageous water loss of conventional locks.

In 1789 a token was struck to commemorate the building of a device (the first of its kind in Britain) which carried boats 'dry' in cradles down a ramp with a vertical fall of 73 feet. The canal was the Ketley, built to carry coal and ironstone to Ketley ironworks. This was a one-way traffic, and the weight of loaded boats moving down the ramp was used to draw returning empty boats up it. This canal was

The upper and lower gates of a narrow lock built in the 1790s on the Warwick and Birmingham Canal (now the Grand Union Canal). The elements of gate construction – frames, irons and balance beams – are clearly delineated from *Utensils in Canal Work*

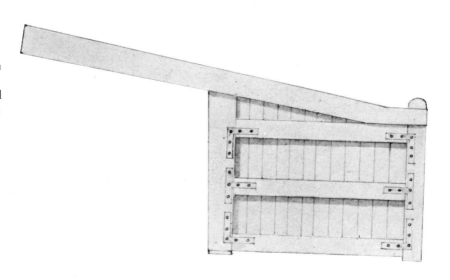

Lower gates of a Lock.

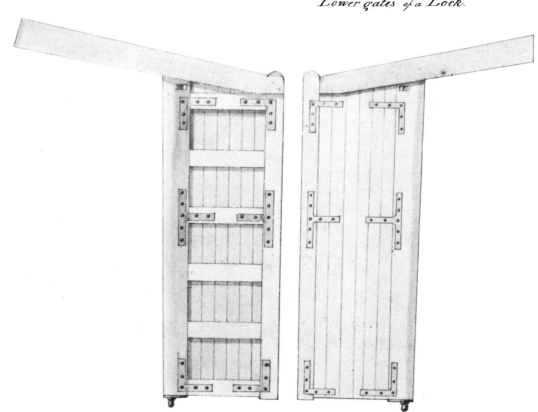

Cast iron work for lock gates.

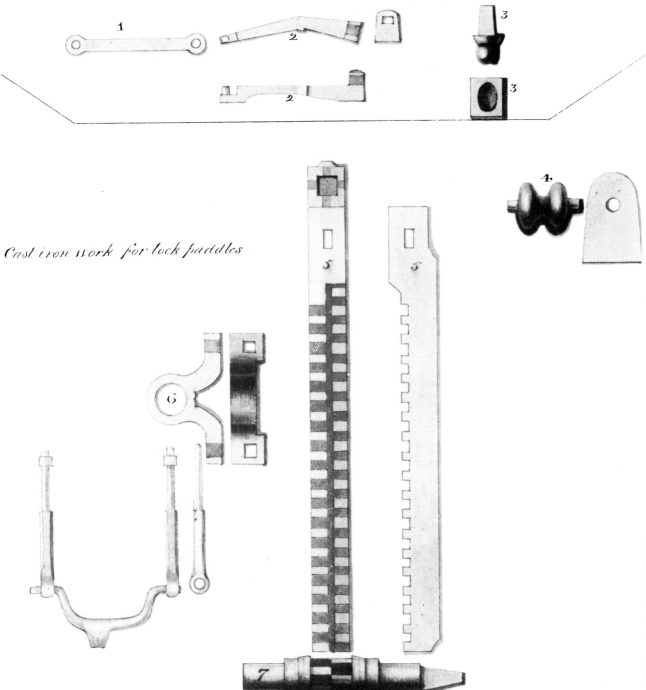

Cast iron work for lock paddles

Patterns for the cast iron work of locks built in the 1790s. Throughout the English canal system many of the original castings are still in use. Shown in the upper part of the illustration are the elements of lock gate collar and tan pin, while below is the paddle gearing from *Utensils in Canal Work*

part of the industrial complex of Coalbrookdale; but, in fact, it was the more agrarian west country that became the testing-ground for apparatus such as this.

At Mells, near Frome, on the Dorset and Somerset Canal, long vanished from sight and memory, 'Fussell's Patent Balance Lock' was erected and, it seems, successfully tested in 1800. A contemporary description records that 'many men of science, impartial and unprejudiced . . . were unanimous in declaring it to be the simplest and best of all methods yet discovered for conveying boats from the different levels and for public utility. The expense of it exceeds but little that of the common lock, over which it has these advantages, viz., it elevates a boat of ten tons burthen and sinks another of equal weight by the same operation 20 feet perpendicular in half the time that one boat passes the common lock and this with a trifling loss of water . . .'

Five 'balance locks' were planned on the same length of canal, but the project foundered, and the only evidence now to be found by the industrial archaeologist is the site of the trial lock and four great pits in a line on the side of a hill. It seems likely from the patent specification that the operation of Fussell's lock could have been similar to those actually in use for some 30 years on the now derelict section of James Green's Grand Western Canal, between Lowdwells and Taunton.

No less than seven lifts, with one inclined plane, were built by Green on this canal, the rises varying from $12\frac{1}{2}$ to $42\frac{1}{2}$ feet vertically. The structure of each consisted of two chambers or 'caissons' in the form of watertight timber troughs hung in a static frame and allowed to move up and down. Both troughs were connected by wires passing over pulleys so that one falling would cause the other to rise. Each level of canal was led into two branches with a gate sealing the ends adjacent to the lift structure. Gates were also fixed at either end of the caissons. The whole apparatus was balanced so that when one caisson was at the bottom canal level the other was two inches lower than the upper level. Boats would be raised and lowered floating and thus, whatever the loads in either caisson, the moving parts would be of equal weight. When the upper sets of gates were opened, water flowed into the higher caisson to make up the levels and at the same time provided the extra weight needed for its descent. Initial inertia was overcome by a hand crank. It will be seen that equilibrium of the structure as so far stated is incomplete, for at rest the connecting wires or chains will be biased to one side or the other. To counteract this, similar chains were connected to the underside of each caisson, being picked up from the ground on ascent at the same rate at which its correspondent was shortening.

One of the main problems overcome in these machines was the making of a watertight joint between the raised caisson and the top section of the canal. This was achieved by a bar, operated through a lever, which forced the whole trough tightly against the canal section. At the bottom, on

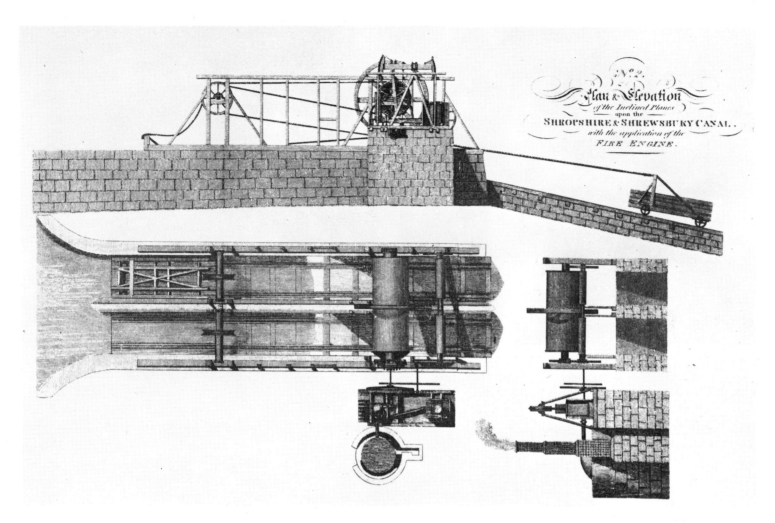

No 2.
Plan & Elevation
of the Inclined Planes
upon the
SHROPSHIRE & SHREWSBURY CANAL.
with the application of the
FIRE ENGINE.

the first six of the seven lifts, the caisson was lowered directly into the canal. It was found, however, that it would not sink far enough to equalise water levels, thus a separate pound lock had to be constructed into which the vessels were floated before finally entering the lower reach. In the last of the lifts at Greenham the principle employed was as at the top, except that the joining faces were cut obliquely, thus the trough wedged itself tightly into position by its own weight. The speed of movement on every lift was controlled by a drum brake.

James Green's lifts worked from 1838 to 1867, but further west still, in Cornwall, an even less orthodox canal had been in use for a decade. The Bude Canal was opened in 1825 from the town of its name to Blagdonmoor (near Launceston), with several branches and six inclined plane lifts. The small boats used on the canal were fitted with wheels which ran in tracks on the face of each ramp. Motive power was provided via ropes from waterwheels at the top level in five cases, and from a water-filled container dropping in a shaft in the sixth. The latter plane, at Hobbacott Down, had a vertical rise of no less than 225 feet. A steam engine was kept in reserve here, lest the mechanics of water power should fail.

In all, 25 examples of lifts and planes were built in south-west England, of which 22 saw fair service, those longest in use – for 60 years in fact – being on the Bude Canal. These figures do not include the crude slides of the St Colomb Canals in Cornwall as they were not apparently used by the boats.

What reason can be given for this development in such a relatively confined region? Firstly, these canals had no direct bearing on the progress of the Industrial Revolution;

Typical side ponds on the Grand Union Canal

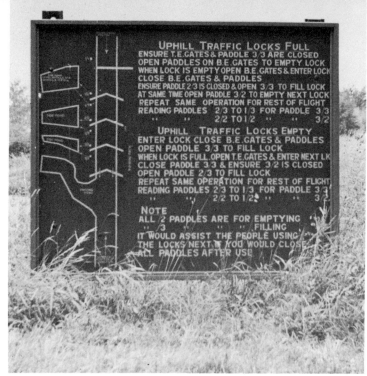

Staircase locks: operating diagram at Watford, on the Leicester section of the Grand Union Canal

they were independent, and late. Not being part of a system, their vessels evolved without cabins and in a smaller form. Trains of 'tub-boats', each boat being 20 to 30 feet long, were pulled by a single horse as easily as a large narrow boat or barge. The long-awaited machines for overcoming changes of level without water loss were more readily constructed for boats of these smaller dimensions. Sadly, and for many of the same reasons, none of these devices, nor their canals, have survived into the present century.

The failure of these machines was ultimately due in no small way to the complication of their structure and operation. 'When the rough usage to which canal locks are subject is considered, and the ignorance of the persons necessarily employed in the management of them, it does not seem probable that any conservative lock will succeed until the whole apparatus shall be reduced to fixed masonry, and no other machinery employed than common gates and paddles, or sluices.' So wrote Joshua Field in 1838, when he put forward his suggestion for an improved canal lock. This was an ingenious but very complex device employing an improbable system of side chambers.

A more practical application of side chambers or 'side ponds' to save water is in fact widely used at locks on many

parts of the system. Quite simply, the lock is emptied into its side pond until levels are equal, when the remainder is run off normally. An amount of water is thereby saved to help fill the lock when next operated. It can be seen that continued use of a single side pond offers no great saving, and more economical variations are twin locks side by side, each acting as a side pond to the other, or several ponds at different levels, being filled alternately from the lock, highest first. Even with twin locks half a lockful may only be saved when the passage is given to a single boat in one direction, or two boats in opposite directions. In fact, on the Trent and Mersey Canal, where such locks exist in part, 'motor-and-butty' traffic working through together effect no saving at all. At the Hanwell Flight, where the Grand Union Canal reaches north London, examples of three side ponds to each lock are encountered, although their use is intermittent, depending on frequency of traffic and availability of water supply.

When a particularly steep slope has to be overcome by a canal, a number of pound locks are often joined together to form a single 'staircase', the top gates to one chamber acting as the bottom gates to the chamber above. Where particularly long staircases are encountered, as at Watford with

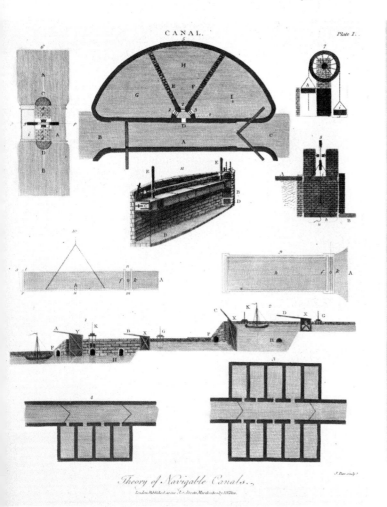

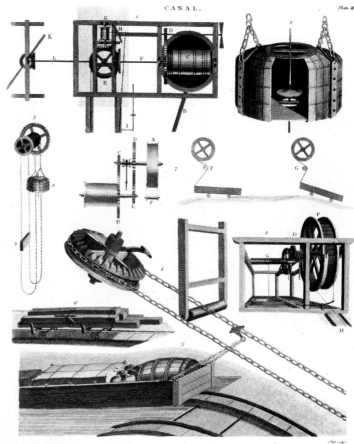

Two plates from *Theory of Navigable Canals*, published in
1800. Shown are the alternative proposals of conventional
pound locks with side-chambers, and lifts and inclines. The
latter were used by James Green on his West-country 'tub-
boat' canals, with limited success

Dundas Aqueduct (1805), after J. C. Nattes. This aqueduct, on John Rennie's Kennett & Avon Canal, is built of Bath stone. The structure spans 150 feet by three arches and features a cornice projecting four feet out from the parapet. A sailing boat is pictured using the canal; an improbable occurrence, in fact, considering the great number of low bridges on this canal

A packet boat crossing Benjamin Outram's Marple Aqueduct over the River Goyt on the Peak Forest Canal. A print issued soon after its completion in 1800

The Watford Staircase

four chambers and Foxton with two sets of five chambers, both on the Leicestershire branch of the Grand Union Canal, side ponds are also employed but in a different capacity. Without them, a boatman at the bottom of an empty flight would be faced with the task of bringing his first lockful of water down through all the chambers above him, so that by the time he had locked up he would have lost a gallonage from the summit level equivalent to the number of chambers in the staircase. In a separated flight, a single lockful only would have been used. The side ponds used are in fact reservoirs with which the ascending boat-man can fill each chamber, but which descending boatmen must keep replenished.

Possibly the earliest example of a staircase with an inter-mediate reservoir is at Bratch, on Brindley's Staffordshire and Worcestershire Canal. Strangely, two complete locks were constructed, the top gates of the lower one being only four feet from those above. The pound between is made sufficient to enable normal working of the locks by being cut at right-angles to the main line of canal.

To terminate the present account of canal locks, reference must be made to a comparatively modern, but very signi-

The Caen Hill flight of locks, Devizes, Kennet and Avon Canal, in the early years of this century

Opposite Boatman Charles Atkins working *Flower of Gloster* through Foxton staircase locks, Grand Union Canal, Leicester section

ficant structure. Significant, because it is the first complete new lock to have been built on the system since the coming of the Manchester Ship Canal; significant also because its design involves prefabrication, and could therefore be the basis of a standard lock design in any new era of canal construction in Britain; but significant, most curiously, because, like the very first pound locks, this latest version has vertically-rising gates.

The Trent and Mersey Canal passes through an area in mid-Cheshire which is subject to subsidence resulting from the pumping of brine. At Thurlwood, near Sandbach, a salt mine some 300 feet from the canal was abandoned in

1927 due to the collapse of a shaft. Also about that time the River Wheelock which ran alongside the shaft changed its course and part of its water discharged down the shaft, so aggravating the already precarious condition in the shaft and mine. In the mid 1930s the effect was felt at the canal; by 1939 repairs to the towing path were becoming extensive; and by 1950 the subsidence had extended to Thurlwood Upper Locks which lie about a quarter of a mile from the disused shaft. It shortly became obvious that works of some magnitude would have to be undertaken to keep the canal open.

Various schemes were considered and it was eventually

Brindley's strange staircase at Bratch, on the Staffordshire and Worcestershire Canal, the top gate of the lower lock being only a few feet from the lower gates of the upper lock

Above A disused lock on the Devizes Flight,
Kennet and Avon Canal
Left Northgate Locks, Chester, on the
Shropshire Union Canal

decided to construct a steel tank based on experience gained at Croxton, where a steel trough replaced a masonry aqueduct across the River Dane to combat a similar type of subsidence. In designing the steel lock the main points to be considered were that it should be self-supporting in the event of differential settlement, that it could be jacked into a straight and level position following subsidence, and that the pit in which the lock was to be erected should be effectively sealed from canal water to prevent flooding.

Thurlwood Steel Lock has a rise of 9 feet 9 inches, and the depths of the upper and lower approaches to the main chamber have been extended sufficiently to allow for a settlement of 2 feet 6 inches before major raising operations need to be undertaken. When the towpath lock had been

The reconstruction of the Thurlwood Steel Lock, 1957

Above and below Thurlwood Steel Lock completed

demolished a mass concrete gravity retaining wall was built to support the offside lock and to form part of the chamber into which the new lock has been built. This wall, 22 feet deep, is backed with clay puddle to ensure watertightness of the offside lock.

Access to the lock operating gear and to craft in the lock is provided by footwalks on both sides, each of which is 4 feet wide and surfaced with asphalt. The sluice pipes and valves are fitted externally, there being two sluices at the upper end to fill the lock and two at the lower end to empty it. All pipes and valves are 1 foot 6 inches in diameter, and in principle are based upon traditional lock equipment.

Balanced steel guillotine gates with L-section rubber seals were selected because of their simplicity, avoiding the need for intricate castings and expensive steelwork in forming quoins, heels and mitres. An important feature of the new lock is that both paddles and gates are fixed with interlock devices so that only one set may be operated at a time.

Thurlwood Steel Lock was opened with some ceremony on 19th May 1958, and although some pleasure boats seem shy of this vertical intrusion of modern engineering into their traditional canal landscape, its performance has been adequate.

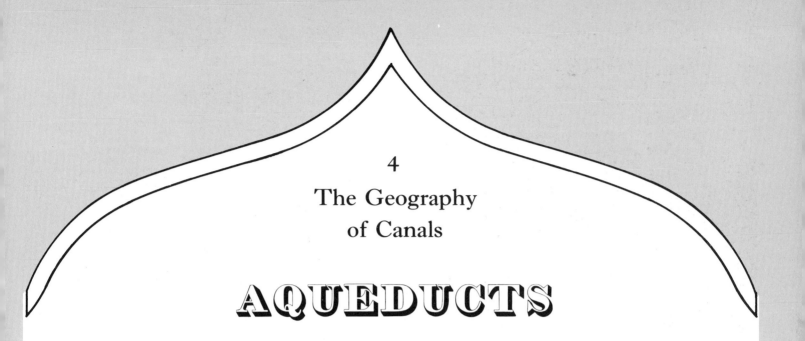

4

The Geography of Canals

AQUEDUCTS

The term 'aqueduct' correctly refers to any artificial water channel, thus in a sense all canals are aqueducts. It is more commonly used now to describe the bridge structure which carries a canal or leat across a valley, river, or other obstacle. This double meaning can lead to confusion when studying older documents, for Joseph Priestly, in an account of the Basingstoke Canal (1831), mentions 'a magnificent aqueduct three-quarters of a mile in length near Aldershott' which, upon exploration, disappointingly turns out to be an embankment. The same feature is described as a viaduct by White in his *History of Hampshire*, 1859. It is an interesting possibility that both of these writers may have been confused by a Roman aqueduct of similar length which once existed not far away, but of which no trace now remains.

In the same vein, a 'canal bridge' was one which carried the waterway over another element, while the 'canal over-bridge' took the element over the waterway. An explanation for this further confusion is found in the constructional form of the conventional aqueduct, the canal towpath and watercourse being carried over the obstacle in a trough which is supported by arches or piers. In one exceptional case, that of the Barton Swing Aqueduct, the trough is cantilevered from a central turntable. The theory of large-scale bridge-building expounded by William Edwards, which was ignored in the humble canal spans, was taken up and brought to an impressive maturity in the aqueducts of Brindley, Outram and their contemporaries.

Brick aqueduct which carried the New River, dating from the 17th century. This is one of the earliest examples of a British aqueduct

The first work of any scale in Britain in which it was required to channel water into an artificial course and pass it over valleys, streams and existing roads, was the New River. Conceived before 1608, this project was to give London a pure water supply replacing decayed and contaminated wells and springs. The work was undertaken by Hugh Myddleton, MP, a merchant with no experience of engineering, who in the words of Smiles 'to quench the thirst of thousands in the populous city of London, fetcht water on his own cost more than 24 miles, encountering all the way an army of oppositions, grappling with Hills, struggling with Rocks, fighting with Forest, till, in defiance of difficulties, he had brought his project to perfection'.

The channel, which ran from Anwell and Chadwell in Hertfordshire to Islington, was ten feet wide and four feet deep. The similarity with the first 'contour canals' is shown by this description: 'to accommodate the cut to the level of the ground as much as possible, numerous deviations were made, and the river was led along the sides of the hills, from which sufficient soil was excavated to form the lower bank'. When a road or stream had to pass beneath the river, continuity was maintained either by arches or timber troughs lined with lead. These timber troughs were, in fact, sustained on embankments which passed culverts through them. The brick arches were the first modern aqueducts in the country. One such, near Edmonton, passed a stream and a road, cost £500 to construct, and was regarded as a major work of its time. The New River, 38¾ miles long as first

constructed, was completed in 1616, and, although much shortened and improved, it still serves its original purpose.

The New River was, more than a century later, of great significance and when the Duke of Bridgewater began to plan a water-road for the passage of his coal from Worsley to Manchester the science of engineering had advanced very little. River navigations had been improved by the further development of the pound lock, but the idea of constructing a water channel of such length that it would be capable of taking loaded barges was unheard of.

As if the undertaking itself was not considered impractical enough, the Duke called in as his engineer one James Brindley, a local millwright who could neither read nor write. He pronounced that the canal should be carried within a watertight trunk of earth on top of a bank crossing the low ground on either side of the River Irwell, and upon reaching that river the trunk should be carried over it on a bridge of stone arches, leaving the river free for navigation. So put upon was the Duke by his friends not to throw away his money on such absurd schemes, that the country's most eminent engineer, Smeaton, was called in to give his opinion. Smeaton's retort was characteristically English: 'I have often heard of castles in the air; but never before saw where any of them were to be erected.'

Brindley's approach was both simple and logical. A canal was a channel dug out of the ground and, if necessary, this channel could be made watertight by a puddled-clay lining. If the canal had to pass at a high level, then the ground

Below 'The Castle in the Air': an engraving of Brindley's first aqueduct at Barton in its early years. *Above left* A more realistic view of the same structure, from a later engraving. *Above right* A photograph taken prior to its demolition in the 1890s. The aqueduct, together with its banked approaches, was 600 feet in length, the centre arch spanned 57 feet, and the two side arches were 32 feet each. The width across the top of the structure was 36 feet, 18 of these being waterway, 6 being puddled lining additional to this and the remainder being packed with earth

Above Dove Aqueduct, on the Trent and
Mersey Canal
Right Another Brindley aqueduct,
carrying the Staffordshire and
Worcestershire Canal

would have to be taken up to that level, and the channel dug out of it. If the canal was to pass over a river navigation, then the ground must be taken over that river on a bridge, and the channel once again excavated. The type of bridge which would have to carry enough earth to accommodate the section of the canal needed to be heavily proportioned; in fact, Brindley's aqueducts were probably unduly massive, as is shown by later examples of lighter construction.

The visual solidity of Barton must have been greatly reassuring to those who had feared inundation from the aqueduct's forecast collapse. When it became apparent that no such catastrophe was forthcoming, the attitude of derision was forgotten and, according to Smiles, 'crowds of people, including those of the first fashion, came to view perhaps the greatest artificial curiosity of the world.'

Brindley built many other notable aqueducts, the most impressive being over the River Dove near Burton-on-Trent on his Grand Trunk (Trent and Mersey) Canal. This, together with its approaches, is a mile and a quarter in length, the waterway being carried on 23 low arches. Because of their heavy form of construction, Brindley's aqueducts could not achieve any great height without the proportions of the supports being gigantic, and therefore totally impracticable. Barton was in fact the highest, the canal being 39 feet above the level of the river. This height restriction was one of the principal reasons for the continuance of the contour method of canal building, where the cut was taken as far as possible on natural levels. Considerable and sometimes tediously winding deviations were made so that it should cross a valley at the easiest point.

The Brecon and Abergavenny Canal, jumping from valley to valley in its clinging descent from the mountainous country of Brecon, crosses no less than six notable masonry aqueducts in only twice as many miles. Wales, with its mountains, its valleys and its industry, was ideal ground for the evolution of canal building and for the perfecting of canal engineering. The proximity of the principal iron-producing districts to most of the projected works in Wales led to the early use of iron for the trunks of aqueducts. By eliminating the heavy clay lining, the proportion of length to height could be extended, thus opening up possibilities for more direct routes hitherto expensive and impracticable.

Iron was to make a pronounced impression upon the structure of the canal system, but only when the system was well established, for the difficulty of transporting it

Brynich Aqueduct near Brecon, where
the Brecon and Abergavenny Canal
crosses the River Usk

over great distances often ruled out any advantage of cheapness. Thus it came about that, long after Telford had erected his iron masterpiece of Pont-y-Cysyllte, 1007 feet long and 120 feet high over the River Dee, masonry continued to be used for canal aqueducts elsewhere.

In 1794 an Act of Parliament was obtained for a canal route from the Ashton Canal at Dukinfield to Peak Forest in Derbyshire. The engineer appointed to this canal was Benjamin Outram, with Thomas Brown as resident engineer in charge of construction. Major natural features which the line had to pass were a hill near Woodley, the valley of the River Goyt (a tributary of the Mersey) which ran 90 feet below the intended level of the canal at Marple, and a rise of 210 feet from the Goyt Valley to the upper pound (Upper Peak Forest Canal), 500 feet above sea-level and now the highest reach of navigable canal in Britain.

A deep cutting was made in the hill between Romiley and Woodley Tunnel, and the contractor for this work was the American inventor Robert Fulton. Fulton put forward many ingenious schemes for linking the two canal levels at Marple, some of them more closely related to mountain railways, but none was considered favourable. He did, however, receive from the Company 100 guineas 'for his many ideas, plans, interest and time with the canal'. Construction had already begun on a more conventional aqueduct of stone designed by Outram but when, in 1800, this had been completed there was little money left for the building of locks. A rope tramway was operated on the

Benjamin Outram's aqueduct at
Marple, carrying the Peak
Forest Canal over the River Goyt

Contemporary engraving of the iron and masonry aqueduct over the River Ceirog at Chirk, crossing the English-Welsh border
Opposite Chirk Aqueduct from the Welsh side

slope between 1798 and 1805, in which year 'The Sixteen' Marple Locks were finally opened.

Marple aqueduct is carried across the Goyt valley on three arches. Outram called upon the precedent of William Edwards by piercing the shoulders of these arches with hollow cylinders, thus lessening the considerable weight of filling which would otherwise have to bear on each pier. The result is, aesthetically, most pleasing, far more so than that of a later railway viaduct beside it which rises higher and is longer. Two types of local stone were used to face the aqueduct, distinguishing by colour the retaining and load-bearing masses from the parapet and purely decorative longitudinal ledges. These latter, which would not have been dreamed of by Brindley, do serve visually to relieve the heaviness of large areas of masonry.

Benjamin Outram had the distinction of being the first engineer to erect an iron aqueduct, located at The Holmes on the Derby Canal. The metal was not at all unfamiliar to Outram, for he had for five years partnered another prominent canal engineer, William Jessop, at the Butterley ironworks. This iron aqueduct was opened in February 1795, one month before that at Longdon-on-Tern on the Shrewsbury Canal designed by Thomas Telford, who claimed of his work: 'I believe this to be the first aqueduct for the purposes of a navigable canal which has ever been composed with this metal.'

Some confusion exists as to who should be credited with the idea of using iron for Telford's aqueducts, not only at Longdon, but also for those two longest and highest canal spans across the Welsh valleys of Ceriog (Chirk) and Dee (Pont-y-Cysyllte) on the Ellesmere Canal. Charles Hadfield, after considerably detailed research, avers that Thomas Eyton, Chairman of the Shrewsbury Canal Committee, suggested its use at Longdon. Thomas Eyton was also Treasurer to the Ellesmere Canal Company, and it is likely that he was involved in discussions on the Welsh aqueducts. Telford, who was a mason, was only the general agent to the company (in fact, 'General Agent, Surveyor, Engineer, Architect and Overlooker of the Works'), whilst Jessop was the engineer, helped by John Duncombe, Thomas Denson and William Turner. Telford was working with ironmasters for the first time.

A description of the Ellesmere Canal is given by Smiles who states that it is:

. . . a series of navigations proceeding from the river Dee in the vale of Llangollen. One branch passes northward, near the towns of Ellesmere, Whitchurch, Nantwich, and the city of Chester, to Ellesmere Port on the Mersey; another, in a south-easterly direction, through the middle of Shropshire towards Shrewsbury on the Severn; and a third, in a south-westerly direction, by the town of Oswestry, to the Montgomeryshire Canal near Llanymynech; its whole extent, including the Chester Canal, incorporated with it, being about 112 miles.

From Whitchurch to Ellesmere, Chirk, Pont-y-Cysyllte, and the river Dee, $1\frac{3}{4}$ miles above Llangollen, the distance is $38\frac{1}{4}$ miles, and the rise 13 feet, involving only two locks. The latter

A contemporary artist's impression of the Pont-y-Cysyllte Aqueduct, carrying the Welsh Canal over the River Dee

Opposite and pages 97–99 The Pont-y-Cysyllte
Aqueduct: 'The aqueduct is approached on the south side by an embankment 1500 feet in length, extending from the level of the water-way in the canal until its perpendicular height at the "tip" is 97 feet; thence it is carried to the opposite side of the valley, over the River Dee, upon piers supporting nineteen arches, extending for a length of 1007 feet. The height of the piers above low water in the river is 121 feet. The lower part of each was built solid for 70 feet, all above being hollow, for the purpose of saving masonry as well as ensuring good workmanship. The outer walls of the hollow portion are only two feet thick, with cross inner walls. As each stone was exposed to inspection, and as both Telford and his confidential foreman, Matthew Davidson, kept a vigilant eye upon the work, scamping was rendered impossible, and a first-rate piece of masonry was the result.'—Samuel Smiles's description

part of the undertaking presented the greatest difficulties; as, in order to avoid the expense of constructing numerous locks, which would also involve serious delay and heavy expense in working the navigation, it became necessary to contrive means for carrying the canal on the same level from one side of the respective valleys of the Dee and the Ceriog to the other.

Besides the physical difficulties, Jessop had also to overcome the objection of owners of land crossed by the proposed canal. The spanning of the Ceriog valley would best have been carried out at Chirk, but an embankment at this point – an aqueduct was not considered feasible in the early planning stages – would have been an obstruction to the view, and it was therefore intended to cross at Pont-faen instead. On 14th July 1795 Jessop recommended to the committee that iron aqueducts should be used at Pont-y-Cysyllte and at Chirk where, he argued, 'instead of an obstruction it will be a romantic feature in the view'. Certainly the use of iron made possible an aqueduct at Chirk, but if that at Longdon – by no means graceful – was anything of a comparison, this would be no less a visual evil than the embankment would have been. Probably for this very reason Chirk Aqueduct appears to be a very finely executed all-masonry structure; the balanced proportions, however, are only made possible by its heart of metal. Telford's own account reads as follows:

The spandrels of the stone arches were constructed with longitudinal walls, instead of being filled in with earth, and across these the canal bottom was formed by cast iron plates at each side, infixed in square stone masonry. These bottom plates had flanches on their edges, and were secured by nuts and screws at every juncture. The sides of the canal were made waterproof by ashlar masonry, backed with hard burnt bricks laid in Parker's cement, on the outside of which was rubble stone work, like the rest of the aqueduct. The towing path had a thin bed of clay under the gravel, and its outer edge was protected by an iron railing. The width of the water-way is 11 feet; of the masonry on each side, 5 feet 6 inches; and the depth of the water in the canal, 5 feet. By this mode of construction the quantity of masonry is much diminished, and the iron bottom plate forms a continuous tie, preventing the side-walls from separation by lateral pressure of the contained water.

Even before Jessop had made his recommendations, the stone was being quarried and worked for an aqueduct of traditional form across the Dee. This would have been on three areas, with the level 24 feet lower than the rest of the waterway, and connected by three locks on either side. Had this scheme been carried out it would probably have been similar in appearance to Outram's Marple Aqueduct.

The foundation-stone of the iron aqueduct was laid only eleven days after the submission of Jessop's report, and before official approval had been given to the design. The span of each iron arch was 45 feet. The trough itself was not a particularly good exercise in prefabrication, for no less than eleven different patterns were used for the side plates alone; 38 of each pattern being required and a total of 418 plates

THE NAVIGABLE AQUEDUCT of PONT Y CYSSYLTE for the ELLESMERE CANAL over the RIVER DEE at the BOTTOM of the VALE of LLANGOLLEN.

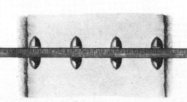

forming the walls of the trough. Telford employed the principles of masonry construction inappropriately here, for the vertical stability which these wedge-shaped plates would have given had they been of stone, is already provided for by iron ribs – again arched – spanning between the piers beneath the trough. Four such ribs, braced laterally, form each arch. The width of canal is 11 feet 10 inches. The towpath is 4 feet 8 inches wide, and consists of an iron grille supported by iron pillars rising from the bed of the channel. As at Chirk, the path side is protected by iron railings. The opposite side is not so protected and the water level is only a few inches below the trough's top edge.

The ceremonial opening of the aqueduct is commemorated by the inscription on a cast-iron plate set in one of the piers:

The Nobility and Gentry of The adjacent Counties, Having united their efforts with The great commercial interests of this Country In creating an intercourse and union between ENGLAND AND NORTH WALES, by a navigable communication of the three Rivers SEVERN, DEE, AND MERSEY, For the mutual benefit of Agriculture and Trade, Caused the first stone of this Aqueduct of PONTCYSYLTE, To be laid on the 25th day of July, 1795, When Richard Myddleton, of Chirk, Esq. M.P. One of the original patrons of the ELLESMERE CANAL, Was Lord of this Manor, And in the Reign of our Sovereign GEORGE THE THIRD, When the equity of the Laws, and The security of Property, Promoted the general welfare of the Nation; While the Arts and Sciences flourished By his Patronage, and The conduct of civil life was improved By his example. The navigation over this Aqueduct was opened 26th November, 1805.

The character of a man may be read in his works. The self-taught pioneer builds boldly and massively without inhibition; the stonemason exhibits his craft when working materials other than stone: what, then, can be said of the works of a formally trained millwright, scholar and university graduate? Smiles writes of John Rennie's Kennet and Avon Canal: 'wherever there is an aqueduct or a bridge upon the line of this canal, it will be found excellent in workmanship and tasteful in design. As a whole, the navigation was one of the best executed in the kingdom . . .' The same praise stands equally for every bridge, aqueduct or tunnel laid down by this engineer.

An engraving of Rennie's Lune Aqueduct, near Lancaster

This canal, opened in 1810, linked the navigations of the Avon and Thames, providing a broad trunk route between east and west coasts, and directly connecting the ports of London and Bristol. The 57-mile section of canal between Newbury and Bath presented some particularly difficult and often unique engineering problems, with the result that it contains many notable structures. There are two architecturally outstanding aqueducts—one at Avoncliff, and the other at Limpley Stoke, known as the Dundas Aqueduct.

A navigable communication between the coal-fields near Wigan and the lime districts about Lancaster, Burton, and Kendal, connecting these towns also with the intervening country as well as with Liverpool, Manchester, and the towns of South Lancashire, had long been regarded as an object of importance. A survey had been made by Mr Brindley as early as 1772, but nothing further was done until some twenty years later, when a company was formed with Mr Rennie as engineer. The line surveyed by him commences near Wigan, and pro-

ceeds northward by Chorley, Preston, and Garstang, to Lancaster, where, skirting the east side of the town, and crossing the Lune by a noble aqueduct, it then passes by Haughbridge to its northern terminus at Kendal; the total length of the main line being 75¾ miles, and the branches two miles more. The aqueduct over the Lune is the principal architectural work on the canal, consisting of five semicircular arches of 75 feet span each; the soffits being 50 feet, and the surface of the canal 62 feet above the average level of the river. The total length of the aqueduct—which forms a prominent feature in the landscape—is 600 feet. The whole is built of hard sandstone, the masonry being in imitation of rockwork, the top surmounted by a handsome Doric cornice and balustrade. It exhibits, in fine combination, the important qualities of strength, durability, and elegance in design; and even at this day it will bear a favourable comparison with the best works of its kind in the kingdom. (Smiles, 1862.)

Aqueducts of stone and iron have been examined in detail; the use of brick was largely confined to spans of no great height. Many of Brindley's aqueducts, including that over the River Dove on the Trent and Mersey Canal, were of brick, although stone was almost always used in preference where it was available locally at an economic price.

There is no evidence of permanent structures being built of timber, apart from some early channelling on Hugh Myddleton's New River. The reasons are obvious enough: lack of strength and durability, and an inability to span very great distances. Brunel, however, was later to prove its engineering worth by using it to support his railway across numerous west country valleys.

The original trough of the aqueduct over the Ouse at Wolverton, on the Old Grand Junction Canal, was of masonry on three arches. It was designed by Jessop, erected by local contractors, and opened in 1805. Before this time, navigation had been carried on by locks on either side of the valley descending to the river level. Pronouncements that the works were faulty proved accurate when, after only a few months, the northern approach embankment blew, flooding a wide area, and more dramatically two years later, when both outer arches collapsed into the river below. A local carpenter partially exonerated his fellows by providing a timber trunk which remained in use for a full year, although the present iron trough was not installed until two and a half years after the collapse. There is some doubt here as to whether the temporary trunk did anything more than continue the water supply to the canal level and traffic was probably redirected through the old locks for the whole of that time.

Aqueduct by Brindley at Longford, Bridgewater Canal

Left A railway aqueduct at Frimley, carrying the Basingstoke Canal
Opposite Iron and masonry at Pont-y-Cysyllte; typical of Telford's fine detailing

The coming of the railway age caused the appearance of a new type of canal structure – the 'railway aqueduct'. Because level-crossings were impossible, railways had to pass either over or under the existing lines of canals. In the latter case, the construction of the aqueducts would have delighted Brindley, for the waterway was usually left undisturbed, complete with its lining and a sufficient amount of surrounding earth, while the railway cutting was carefully excavated around and under it, the exposed sections being finally lined with engineering brick.

A fine example of a railway aqueduct is to be found at Frimley, in Surrey, where the old London and South-Western Railway passes under the Basingstoke Canal. The aqueduct has a lively history: design and construction were undertaken by the railway company during the 1830s, and all proceeded normally, the cutting being taken to the face of the proposed section, and arches for each of the two railway tracks being bored and lined. As the canal bed was not lined at this point, water traffic had to stop while a brick invert and clay were put in above the arches. In about 1900 the railway was widened to four tracks, and two more arches were similarly added beneath the canal. All proved well until 1925, when a settlement was noticed in the towpath over one of the railway lines. A leak developed and steadily grew worse; water was running down the back of the brickwork and gushing out of the drainage holes onto the footplates of the locomotives as they went through the arches. The manager of the railway contacted the owner

of the canal, Mr A J Harmsworth, and it was decided to re-line the canal bed. Regular traffic had by this time ceased on the canal west of the aqueduct, but a supply of water had to be kept running over it so that barge traffic could continue at the Woking end. To accommodate this Mr Harmsworth designed and supervised the building of dams on either side of the railway, connected by a 190-foot long braced timber duct which by-passed the works to the main structure.

It was found during the course of the works that the leak had occurred at the junction of the original structure with the 1900 extension. The re-lining was carried out by railway staff, the canal bed being first dug out, re-bricked and puddled, then lined with lead sheets having soldered joints; more clay was set on this before the final brick invert was replaced. At this time, also, side walls and a safety handrail were added to the channel but the external appearance of the aqueduct remained unchanged throughout the whole operation.

Entirely utilitarian though these structures were, their accomplishment at such an early stage in the development of civil engineering inspired much awe and wonder. Describing the Barton Aqueduct an eighteenth-century writer expressed some surprise that he 'saw several barges of great burthen drawn by a single mule along a river hung in the air, and over another river underneath, by the side of which some ten or twelve men might be seen slowly hauling a single barge against the stream'.

An aqueduct and embankment on the
Macclesfield Canal

A canal fly-over – the Macclesfield
Canal crosses the Trent and
Mersey Canal

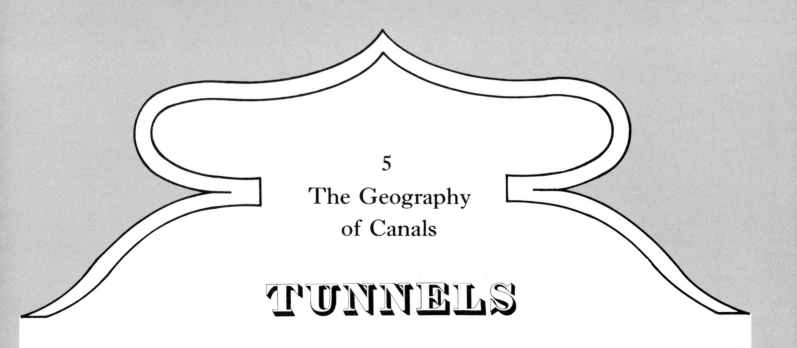

5
The Geography of Canals

TUNNELS

In Samos there were, 524 years B C, found engineers capable of perforating a high mountain with a tunnel of eight feet in height, and the same in breadth, and seven furlongs in length, containing an aqueduct which supplied the town with excellent water.

Thus reported the *European Magazine* of October 1810. In the same issue, an advertiser urged readers to make a speedy application for shares in the 'New Universal Tunnel Company' as they 'will soon obtain a most enormous premium'. The aim of this company, it seems, was to open up communications between all parts of the earth by the most direct routes – tunnelling through it. The advertisement goes on to dispel any doubts that might be raised in the minds of prospective subscribers that such a project could succeed; obstacles, such as an encounter with 'the dwelling of the damned' or 'a vast mass of calorific' are lightly dismissed, and the briefest sympathies only are expressed for the poor tunneller when the centre of gravity had been passed, who, 'after having hitherto worked in the regular manner, with his feet downwards, will be necessitated to strike with his axe at the substances immediately above him'.

Sadly, there is no record of any cutting being made on this project, but we do know that the company managed to raise a substantial capital. The very existence of such a company, only 50 years after the concept of a modest canal aqueduct had been almost universally ridiculed as a 'castle in the air', exemplifies well the enormous advances made in civil engineering techniques in that time. It is less surprising that these advances should be more notable in the field of tunnelling, for it is one of the instincts of man to look underground for his wealth and welfare. Britain has abundant evidence of this, in the numerous burrows and caves excavated for hearthstone, ironstone and sandstone in the south, in her coalfields, and in the incredible perforations of the south-west, whose shafts reach 500 fathoms below the surface with galleries probing for metal a mile or more under the sea bed west of Land's End. The legend that at the bottom of every hole is a Cornishman is not without foundation, for it is in this westernmost county that mining techniques universally used have their origin and evolution.

Coal was the basis of the Canal Age, and the fuel of the Industrial Revolution. It is therefore appropriate that the earliest and most extensive canal tunnels were to be found in the coal mines of the Duke of Bridgewater. The first act of cutting the Duke's Canal was the excavating of a basin at Worsley Mill, adjacent to the coal mine, as a reservoir to the projected canal. From this basin a passage was dug for

Setting out a tunnel, from *Utensils in Canal Work*

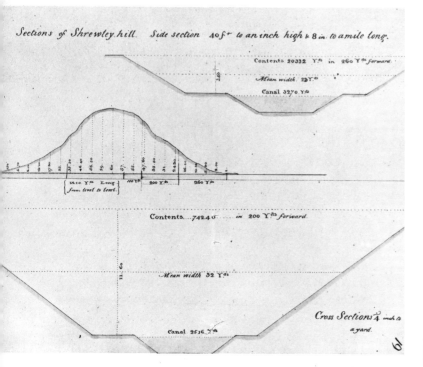

Left and above Chirk Tunnel, on the Welsh Canal

three-quarters of a mile into the side of the hill, through which boats were passed. The boats using the underground canal were flat-bottomed, divided into a number of compartments containing boxes of coal. At the basin these boxes were easily unloaded with crane or lifting-gear into barges and wagons, an instance of 'containerisation' which remained almost unique on the canals until modern times. The mine's water channels were fitted with handrails on the side walls, by which means the boats could be drawn along. In many of the later canal tunnels not provided with towpaths this method was to be copied.

Civil engineering was to progress appreciably during the

The Armitage Tunnel, cut through solid rock, on the Trent and Mersey Canal

next few decades. It was also to lose gradually the interest of popular journalism, for industrial communities were being established in which the near-impossible was becoming the commonplace. Engineers themselves moved in the closed circles of their Institutions and Societies where they could expound and record, faithfully and often boringly, all the technicalities of their latest achievements. Thus, while Pont-y-Cysyllte is likened rather obliquely by Tennyson to 'the full flowering of the Gothic', the earliest experiments of Brindley were considered so remarkable

that all who could might read the most detailed and colourful accounts of the progress of the works.

One such account, in the *European Magazine,* describes the works at Worsley:

This passage being a curious and interesting work of art we shall describe it: In some places it is cut through the solid rock, and in others arched with brick. There are several air-tunnels cut through near forty yards deep, at certain distances, to give air: the entrance is six feet wide, and about five feet high above the water; it widens in some places for boats to pass. The coals

An early photograph (c. 1900) of leggers emerging from a tunnel

are brought to the boats in low carriages; and, as the passage is on a descent, although they hold a ton each, they are easily drawn along by men, on a railed way, to a stage over the canal, and then shot into the boats. These boats, which contain about seven tons each, are easily drawn out of the passage, where two, three, or more are linked together, and drawn by horses or mules to the place of their destination.

. . . You enter with lighted candles the subterraneous passage in a boat, made for bringing out the coals, forty-seven feet long, four feet and a half broad, including the gun-wales, and two feet six inches deep. This boat, when loaded, carries about seven tons, and sometimes eight. In this manner you proceed up the canal to the lake at the head of the mine, distant three quarters of a mile: the two folding-doors at the mouth are immediately shut on your entrance, to keep out too much air, if the wind blows: and you then proceed by the light of your candles, which cast a vivid gloom, serving only to make darkness visible.

But this dismal gloom is rendered still more awful by the solemn appearance of this subterranean lake, which returns various and discordant sounds. At one moment you are struck with the grating noise of engines, which, by a curious contrivance, let down the coals into the boats. At another you hear the shock of an explosion, occasioned by the blowing up of the hard rock, which will not yield to any force other than that of gunpowder; immediately after, perhaps, your ears are saluted by the songs of merriment from either sex, who thus beguile their labours in these gloomy caverns.

When you have reached the head of the works, a new scene opens to your view: there you behold men and women, almost in their primitive state of nature, toiling in different capacities, by the glimmering of dim tapers, some digging the jetty ore out of the bowels of the earth, some again loading it in wagons, made for the purpose, others drawing the wagons to the boats.

As far as possible canal engineers tended to avoid large-scale works of cutting and embanking because of lack of knowledge, but the same cannot be said for tunnelling. A wealth of mining experience existed and this was called upon in the areas of early canal development. It was the miner who tunnelled through, working precariously with gunpowder, by the light of naked flames, and in close proximity to bonfires kept burning under vertical shafts to provide updraughts for ventilation. Once the way had been blasted out the techniques became less orthodox, principally because the canal tunnel had to be straight whereas the mine gallery did not. Further, there must be no danger of the tunnel collapsing, and so unless it was being driven directly through solid rock the whole section had to be lined, usually with three layers of brick of a minimum effective thickness of $13\frac{1}{2}$ inches. A brick invert

was often necessary on the canal bed to prevent the new forces of the arch from acting upwards through the bottom. Similarly, external forces had to be overcome. Where the tunnel passed close to mining activity, shafts and galleries had purposely to be avoided or abandoned and sealed off, necessitating compensation payments, while continuing mining activity in close proximity to the tunnel brought about the danger of subsidence and collapse.

Long tunnels were not driven straight through from one end to the other, for such a process would present great practical difficulties in moving spoil horizontally in a re-restricted width of bore, besides being a very lengthy operation with only one contractor working at one time at the head of the bore. Instead, a direct line was taken over the hill or obstruction and vertical shafts sunk at distances of between one furlong and six hundred feet, the actual tunnel being cut out in both directions from the base of each shaft. The accuracy of this cutting is something to be marvelled at when the crudity of tools and levels then available is taken into account. To set out a perfectly straight line over uneven country is a remarkable enough feat (although curiously the track-builders of prehistory were adept at this), but to sink a number of shafts from this uneven ground to the same given depth and link them, so creating a subterranean passage that follows exactly that line above ground, is almost incredible.

For short tunnels, where the obstacle was not deep, an open cutting would first be made, the arch built over, and

THE DOUBLE LOCK, & EAST ENTRANCE
TO THE ISLINGTON TUNNEL, REGENT'S CANAL.

ꝛꝛ. H. Shepherd.   Engraved by F

An engraving of 1827 showing the double lock, and east
entrance to the Islington Tunnel, Regent's Canal

the cutting again filled. This method of construction is known as 'cut and cover'. It was thought that such tunnels, while more expensive to build than cuttings, would be cheaper to maintain. Later, engineers capable of making slip-free cuttings reversed the process and, in some cases, even opened out these original tunnels.

The tunnels themselves are testimony enough to the skill of their builders; there are few, apart from Brindley's very earliest, where the segment of light from one end cannot be clearly seen from the other, although it may be more than a mile distant.

The constructing of a large number of shafts meant that

more gangs of labourers were able to work on the project at one time. The immediate extra expense of this heavy employment was more than offset by the factor of speed, for the sooner navigation was opened the sooner would tolls and dividends be forthcoming. As it was, when difficult terrain had to be passed, the tunnel was inevitably the last link in the whole line of canal to be opened. Late canals, hoping to rival the less direct routes of others, or even threatened by the prospect of railway competition, would obviously suffer greatly from any delay.

Blisworth Tunnel, the longest one now open on a through navigation, caused much trouble to its constructors. Begun in 1793 on a line slightly longer than that now existing, work came to a stop after three years because of excessive water and poor materials. The resident engineer, Barnes, together with Whitworth and Rennie, suggested the present line, but because of financial difficulties could not proceed with it until 1802. The rest of the canal had been completely open by 1800. Traffic was carried over Blisworth Hill, first by the construction of a toll road, and later, in November 1800, by the opening of a double-track horse-tram road built by Benjamin Outram (from whose name is said to be derived the word 'tram'). This proved serviceable, though not completely satisfactory as it involved a transhipment of goods at each end, but it was a further five years before the new tunnel was opened, drains having first been constructed under the level of the bore to run off excess water.

While hindering works in progress the presence of water in tunnel borings was often a factor relied upon, or hoped for, by a canal engineer. Whilst a canal might be re-routed to avoid heavy cutting, this was not always so with tunnels. In fact, where the water supply was uncertain, the possibility of striking underground springs by going through a hill instead of round it was an important influence in the setting out of canal summit levels.

The Basingstoke Canal was planned originally to loop round Greywell Hill, west of Odiham, thereby serving the neighbourhood of Turgis Green and adding about six miles to the present line. There was a definite problem of water supply to this canal, however, as there was little or no high ground in the surrounding area suitable for catchment and reservoir construction. Certainly this has resulted in an unusually long summit level of $21\frac{1}{2}$ miles between Aldershot and Basingstoke, which acts in part as its own reservoir. The canal falls by 29 wide locks to the River Wey, and

Opposite Greywell Tunnel, Basingstoke Canal; the eastern end

Below Greywell Tunnel, western end, about 1920 (now collapsed). The contrast in the portals is explained by the number of gangs of labourers employed in the construction: invariably both ends would be undertaken at the same time, and although both portals might contain the same elements of design, the interpretation of each is different

a steady supply had to be ensured to accommodate the possible heavy traffic. Thus it was decided to tunnel through the chalk of Greywell, both to shorten the route and in the hope of striking springs, a move which was to prove successful. Because the tunnel yielded the canal's principal water supply, it could not be shut off and drained to permit inspection and repair without bringing all navigation to a stop. To overcome this a crude form of demountable platform was used, which consisted of planks laid on baulks of timber carried across the section and anchored in small square recesses above water-level on either side of the arch. These recesses occur every few yards, and the amount of re-pointing and re-lining which can be seen to have been carried out during its lifetime suggests that the tunnel either suffered considerably from earth movement or was very poorly built in the first place. The latter is quite likely, for John Pinkerton, the contractor for this canal, was required by the proprietors to use local labour wherever possible, and it is recorded that 'these industrious poor' in this purely agricultural area 'are by all their efforts incapable of earning a sustenance' at the work.

In contrast, the maintenance of Blisworth Tunnel was carried out using far more sophisticated methods. A movable cross dam was used, consisting of two barriers. These were constructed in such a way that they were in outline shape similar to the internal section of the tunnel below water level. The two were placed at either end of the section requiring repair, forced into the irregularities of

the tunnel walls for water-tightness, and the intermediate 'pound' so formed was pumped dry. In practice, the pumps would have been kept at work continually, taking up leakage through the barriers and the entry of water from springs and down ventilation shafts, which were themselves sometimes pierced by springs. This cross dam was last used in about 1920. To carry out similar repairs today, stop planks are inserted across the tunnel mouth at the north end, and the whole length is emptied by draining the water down through the locks at Stoke Bruerne.

From the shafts sunk originally to cut the tunnels, ventilation shafts were made, usually being lined afterwards to prevent inward collapsing. When first cut these shafts were similar to mine shafts and, as in mines, horse gins were used to raise the buckets of spoil cut out by manual labour. In most cases the spoil mounds which then grew up beside the shafts were left untouched and remain to this day although much overgrown. Often these mounds may be seen where there is no ventilation shaft which proves that more shafts were used in the construction period than were later converted to air shafts, for obviously it was much cheaper to fill in a shaft than it was to line it. It must also be remembered that most tunnels were built when all traffic was horse-drawn and most boats were day boats (without a cabin), and thus even the pollution of smoke from a cabin stove was hardly considered. More than one tragedy was occasioned, at the inception of steam power and steam tunnel tugs, by the asphyxiation of the steerer, the boat

Contrasting tunnel portals: Preston Brook Tunnel, Trent and Mersey Canal, south end (*above*) and north end (*opposite*)

then guiding itself through the straight bore to emerge gruesomely with a corpse at the tiller.

Greywell Tunnel has no ventilation shafts, the reason for which was most probably to keep the costs down. The fact that the tunnel was nevertheless built in sections, and from shafts, is plain to see from within, for every 600 feet there is a noticeable kink in the walls, indicating where gangs working from opposite directions joined up slightly out of line. In spite of its apparent lack of internal ventilation the bore of the tunnel was considered a healthy enough place to spend a night. The bargemen, who worked

regularly down the canal from the brickworks above the tunnel during the closing years of the last century, would time their passage so that they entered the west portal at nightfall. The slight flow caused by the springs would take the barge through by morning, when the boatman would carry on his way, having spent a well sheltered night.

Navigation of this tunnel came to an end in 1934 when the overflows from an ornamental pond on the hill above the tunnel became blocked. The resulting water pressure caused an island and a tree that were in the centre of the pond to fall through the tunnel roof. Regular commercial

traffic above Odiham had ceased by this time, thus nothing was done to repair the collapse. For a few years the only obstacle was the trunk of the tree protruding into the bore, and it was possible to navigate a small boat round this. Further water pressure then began to force clay along the tunnel in both directions from the fall so that now there is a blockage of some 700 feet. The west portal collapsed in the 1950s, probably from the weight of tree roots in the surrounding cutting, but as the canal has not been closed, the tunnel may well be re-opened at some future time.

The entire length of the Trent and Mersey, as originally planned by Brindley, was to have been 'narrow', passing boats of only seven feet in width. The principal reason for this was that the canal had to negotiate Harecastle Hill by a tunnel $1\frac{1}{2}$ miles long. There was no precedent for wide tunnels as miners had been used only to cutting out low and narrow galleries. The only previous example was at Worsley, and it was on the colliery canals that Brindley based the design of Harecastle, and on the colliery boats, with their width of little more than six feet, that he developed what was to become the standard 'narrow boat'.

Harecastle Tunnel was begun in 1766 and took eleven

Above Ellesmere Tunnel, on the Welsh Canal
Opposite Brindley's Harecastle Tunnel, on the Trent and Mersey Canal, superseded by Telford's tunnel of 1827

years to complete. Water was met in great quantity, and an early form of beam engine was used for pumping as well as the more usual wind and water pumps. Brindley copied his earlier work at Worsley by building, inside the tunnel, branches to his own colliery at Golden Hill. The boats used for these passages, like those at Worsley, were shorter than the standard narrow boats and carried only ten tons so that they could negotiate the right-angled turns at the junctions. Brindley died in 1772 and the work was carried to completion by his brother-in-law, Hugh Henshall.

Few of the longer bores were able to accommodate both channel and towpath because of their narrowness. Berwick Tunnel on the Shrewsbury Canal, opened in 1797, was the first one of any great length (970 yards) to do so. The engineer of this canal was Josiah Clowes, succeeded on his death in 1795 by Telford. William Reynolds was consulting

Telford's Harecastle Tunnel before the rebuilding of 1974–77, north end; Brindley's earlier tunnel can be seen to the right

engineer and it was he who suggested that the towpath should be continued through the tunnel.

The long, narrow tunnel without a path was the most obstructive feature of any canal route. Passing inside the tunnel was usually impossible and traffic in both directions was held up while one boat proceeded either way, for the earliest system of traffic flow was passing a single boat alternately in each direction. This was soon amended, however, on most tunnels, to a 'period' system similar to that partially in use today, where boats could pass in either direction only between certain specified hours. Boatmen aware of the favourable times of entry would determine their passages accordingly although this did not prevent frequent disputes amongst the 'very rough class of labourers', as Smiles unkindly called them. However, this problem was occasionally overcome, as on the Strood Tunnel on the Thames and Medway Canal, which although built at first in one continuous length of more than two miles, was opened out after one year of working to provide a 30-yard section of passing space. Standedge Tunnel was built with several passing spaces.

On less heavily worked canals, where there was seldom the need and never the manpower to enforce sophisticated regulations, a rule-of-thumb was observed in the event of two boats meeting inside a tunnel. A mark would be made on the wall halfway through the bore and the first boat past it had right of passage. A local writer tells of a case at Greywell when two boats met at the mark:

. . . neither of the *captains* would give way. The owner of one barge, a miller, near Odiham, sent in a boat with provisions and beer for his men, and so starved their opponents into surrender.

A horse-drawn boat had to be propelled through a tunnel without a towpath, by 'shafting' or 'legging'. Shafting consisted of pushing with a long pole or shaft against the top or sides of the tunnel while walking from forward to aft of the boat; it was generally performed only in short tunnels with a suitably large section of bore. 'Leggers' would lie horizontally on narrow boards sprung out from either side of the forward end of the boat, and by walking along the sides of the tunnel push it through. The boards were termed 'wings', and a well-equipped boat carried two pairs, short and long, for narrow and broad tunnels. Professional leggers were often employed by the canal companies, each working only one way through one particular tunnel. Where these services were not available, the crew would have to undertake the task, meaning usually the boatman and his wife. This could be both unpleasant and

Telford's Harecastle Tunnel, south end, showing the pumping station and height gauge

hazardous, particularly in Brindley's Harecastle Tunnel, where lack of knowledge of the colliery branch could result in an unforseen immersion. Falling overboard in a tunnel could be fatal, for the boatman by tradition was unable to swim, and besides the danger of drowning there was that of being crushed between the boat and the tunnel wall. It was not uncommon practice, indeed on some canals it was compulsory, for leggers to strap themselves on to the wings.

Horse-paths were always provided over the tunnels. Where there was an accumulation of boats waiting to pass through, particularly when tugs were introduced, all the horses would be led over in a train by one person, for a small fee, or possibly by returning leggers. Sometimes, if a path was fenced and there was little danger of straying, the well-trained horse would be left to go over on its own, and would be found waiting for the boat, and its perspiring master, at the other end. Legging was tiring and time-consuming, a fact which in no way helped traffic flow. Even the professional leggers at Harecastle 'were usually completely exhausted, and as wet from perspiration as if they

had been dragged through the canal itself'. The single passage involved three hours' work for a reward of one shilling and sixpence.

It was not long before proposals were put forward for the improvement of navigation of the Trent and Mersey Canal by eliminating or widening the bottleneck of Harecastle. However, nothing was done until plans for rival canals and railways threatened the carrying trade. Telford was called in and recommended a new tunnel parallel to the old. In contrast to its forerunner, the new tunnel took only two years to build, being opened in 1827. It was evidently a masterpiece of its time, Smiles describing it as 'in so perfectly straight a line that its whole length can be seen through at one view; and though it was constructed by means of fifteen different shafts sunk to the same line along the length of the tunnel, the workmanship is so perfect that the joinings of the various lengths of brickwork are scarcely discernible'. Certainly, with the use of both tunnels, the convenience afforded to traffic was considerable. Telford himself, on a survey in 1829, asked a boatman how he liked it. 'I only wish', came the reply, 'that it reached all the way to Manchester!'

Passage of the new tunnel was allowed from south to north only, boats travelling to the Potteries and beyond still having to leg through the old. There is no record of the reactions of the towing animals in being forced to undergo such a damp and unnatural passage beneath Harecastle Hill. De Salis informs us (in 1928, when almost all

Sapperton Tunnel on the Thames and Severn Canal, shown on a token

traffic was still horse-drawn) that 'when the tug is not working, the boats are bow-hauled through'.

Proposals for providing a tug through this tunnel came in 1891 when a Bill was introduced in Parliament to widen the canal from Preston Brook to Stoke-on-Trent, which would have meant removing the towpath through Harecastle. These proposals were never carried out, and when powers were finally given, in 1904, for compulsory haulage through the tunnel 'by an electric or other tug not driven by steam', it was because the earlier tunnel was becoming increasingly more difficult to work through as adjacent mining activity had caused a great deal of subsidence to the roof. Steam was not allowed because of the lack of ventilation, although this form of propulsion had been in use early on canals, especially on tunnel tugs. A towing boat worked by a steam engine of small power was started through Islington Tunnel, Regents Canal, in 1826. It hauled itself along a chain laid on the canal bed, and was capable of pulling four 50-ton barges through in 30 minutes. One reason for this form of movement being used in tunnels was that it considerably simplified or eliminated steering.

This principle was even considered for normal haulage outside tunnels. In 1878 it was proposed to install a rope, along which the tug would haul itself, in the bed of the River Trent from Gainsborough to Nottingham. Similar plans had been put forward in 1852 for the Severn where flexible iron bands were to be laid between Gloucester and Welshpool, a tug picking them up and passing them through powered rollers. What would happen at locks was not made clear, however, and neither scheme was put into practice. The system has been used, with some success, on Continental navigations.

L T C Rolt tells vividly of the difficulties of navigating a motor narrow boat through Braunston Tunnel: 'The stern of the boat is lit by the light streaming in through the mouth of the tunnel, but the bow, seventy feet ahead, is swallowed up in an impenetrable darkness which the eye strains in vain to pierce. Sense of direction is temporarily lost, and by a curious illusion the boat appears to swing rapidly in a circle.' Such an illusion could well lead the inexperienced helmsman to follow a truly erratic course, perhaps colliding with the tunnel walls. Besides being dangerous to any boat coming through in the other direction, this certainly could not but harm the retaining structure of the tunnel and collapses were not infrequent. Thus it was in the companies' own interests that a straight course be maintained by all. On the earlier Trent and Mersey Canal tunnels, Preston Brook, Barnton and Saltersford, all of which tended to meander, the tugs had horizontal wheels which made contact with the tunnel walls, the effect being similar to chain haulage.

It is unfortunate that such consideration for the fabric of the tunnel is not always afforded by a minority of present-day boatmen, who, on entering, leave the tiller and retire inside the cabin to brew tea. Woe betide the unsuspecting

Sapperton Tunnel prior to restoration

pleasure cruiser faced with the near-spectral phenomenon of a driverless narrow boat bearing down upon him, its approach being heralded by a series of fearful thuds as the vessel cannons resoundingly from wall to wall!

A variation in tunnel haulage was tried at Blisworth and Braunston in 1869, when continuous moving wire ropes were installed through both bores. These were powered by stationary steam engines. The complications of boats joining and leaving the ropes may be visualised, and the service was replaced by tugs after only two years. Previous to this, in 1861, an accident involving a company steam-boat occurred in Blisworth, where two men were killed by suffocation. As a result the four ventilation shafts then existing were increased to five, and later to seven.

Most tugs went out of use in the 1930s, when horse-drawn traffic had so declined that the services could no

The Harecastle Tug. When this tug started work, on 30th November 1914, it was accompanied by a barge carrying batteries weighing 18 tons to power two 15 h.p. electric motors on the tug. These turned winches which fed through the running cables. In 1920 current was passed directly to the boat by means of overhead cables. Thirty boats could be taken through at one time, a charge of sixpence per boat, regardless of type or load, being the levy. Use of the tug was compulsory for both horse-drawn and powered craft, for it was feared that if the latter were allowed to use their engines they might catch the running cable in their propellers. The tug remained in use until 1954

longer be justified. Harecastle was exceptional, however, in that the tug remained until 1954. The reason was partly in the inadequate ventilation, but also partly in the danger of subsidence, making unguided navigation dangerous, and the towpath was in bad repair. The installation of a pumping station at the south end in 1954 has overcome this first problem, but the towpath has disappeared in many places, and the roof continues to become lower, necessitating a gauging device at either end. This has not prevented a few instances of boats becoming wedged hard under the low point when the only method of release is to 'run off' water from the summit pound of the canal until the level is sufficiently lowered.

Navigating the Harecastle Tunnel alone before its complete internal restoration of 1974–77 was an experience which Robert Aickman once likened to 'crossing the line'. Besides the irregularities of the roof itself, dipping to its lowest point 1300 yards in, there was the sense of complete isolation as doors at the southern end were shut behind the traveller to make pumping effective. In the summer the thick, red water was usually packed with weed floated down from the Macclesfield Canal; there was the old towpath frequently dipping below water, only to rise up suddenly, seemingly in mid-channel, further on. If all these failed to alarm, then there was the good chance of an encounter with Kit Crew, an unnerving phantom who lurked at the Turnrail, the point at which Telford's tunnel intersected the colliery branch to Golden Hill.

Sapperton Tunnel – the western
portal at the turn of the century

Harecastle is the one tunnel on the canal system which has retained resident keepers to check and regulate passages. Nearly all other remaining tunnels have a wide enough section to permit the passing of narrow boats within, although Barnton, Saltersford and Preston Brook on the Trent and Mersey Canal, and many of the much shorter tunnels, have to be seen to be clear before entry.

The colliery canals at Worsley, upon which James Brindley founded his fame and the Duke of Bridgewater his fortune, eventually extended to a total of 46 miles, probably the greatest length of underground water transport system anywhere in the world. The complex is on three levels, interconnected by shafts and an inclined plane up which the boats themselves were drawn. Although the workings are now disused, many of the passages remain navigable and may be inspected by the curious.

The longest tunnel to be built on a through navigation also has the distinction of being at the highest level attained by canal engineers in Britain. This is Standedge Tunnel, 3 miles and 135 yards long, which pierces the Pennine ridge 644 feet above sea-level on the summit of the Huddersfield Narrow Canal. The cutting, directed by Benjamin Outram, must have been a formidable undertaking; working shafts in places had to be sunk more than 600 feet from the ground above to reach the level of the canal. The bore is lined only in parts, and its narrowest dimensions are 6 feet 8 inches high and 7 feet 1 inch wide at water level. Large caverns were opened out at intervals for boats to pass. The canal was closed in 1944, but Standedge remains passable, as it must, for it drains and ventilates two railway tunnels running adjacent to it and at a slightly higher level. The bore has cast-iron distance plates fixed to the roof every 50 yards. Each portal has been guarded by iron gates since 1951.

The last tunnel to be built on a canal in Britain is also the most sophisticated. Netherton Tunnel, just under two miles long, has two towpaths and is the widest of any canal tunnel, being 27 feet at water level, with a water width of 17 feet. The tunnel was the major part of a branch canal designed to shorten the Dudley-Birmingham route; accommodation had long been afforded by the Old Dudley Tunnel, but its small size and the increase of the traffic rendered it insufficient. Legging through the old tunnel, 3200 yards, was performed by two men, charging three shillings and sixpence for each boat and taking $3\frac{1}{2}$ hours. The Act of Parliament for the branch was obtained in 1855. James Ralph Walker was appointed resident engineer, and the sinking of the first shaft was commenced on 17th January 1856. On 19th March excavation of the tunnel was commenced at Shaft 15; on 4th April the first brick was laid on the south side length at Shaft 15; on 25th March 1858 the last brick was laid by Walker in the arch of the junction length, between Shafts 7 and 8; and on 20th August 1858 the whole of the works was formally opened for traffic. The works provided $2\frac{1}{2}$ miles of canal of which $\frac{1}{4}$-mile was of embankment, $\frac{1}{2}$-mile of open cutting, and $1\frac{3}{4}$ miles of tunnel. The waterway is 6 feet deep at centre,

Penetrating the depths of the collapsed Greywell Tunnel

and the height from water level to the soffit of the tunnel is 15 feet 9 inches. The thickness of brick lining is 1 foot 1½ inches in the invert. In places where the ground was found to be bad the thickness of walls and arch was increased to 2 feet 3 inches. Nine men were killed and 18 seriously injured during the construction of the tunnel.

The total cost of the works was £200,000 including £155,000 for the tunnel. The crowning glory of Netherton was its lighting system, gas at first, and later electricity. A sorry contrast, indeed, was the pale glimmer of tallow dips which had to suffice navigators in their half-certain and painful passage of earlier, oppressive, but pioneering bores.

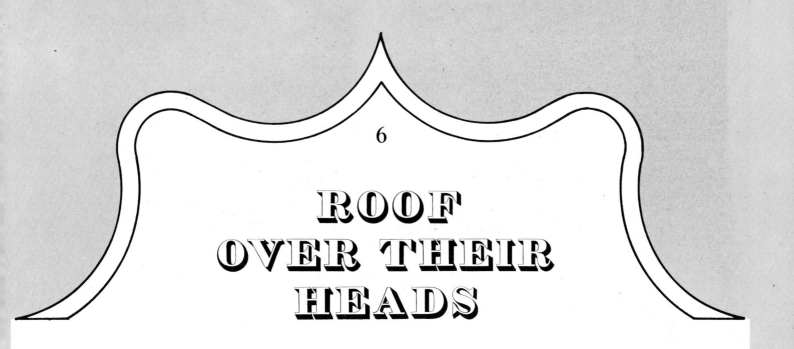

ROOF OVER THEIR HEADS

6

... There are in this country over 100,000 men, women and children, living and floating on our rivers and canals, in a state of wretchedness, misery, immorality, cruelty, and evil training that carries peril with it ...

GEORGE SMITH, 1875.

Notorious in his day but now hardly remembered, George Smith of Coalville was a fanatical Victorian campaigner. Ever pressing for reform but, in fact, in the deepest sense a conservative, when he once found a way of life which his mind failed to grasp, or his imagination permit, then he would publicly denounce it and attempt to hound it out of all existence.

So it was with the canal population. The lot of the boat people was, by his standards, a poor and insanitary one.

The boatman plied his trade over routes which often involved many days' continuous journeying. Because of his nomadic existence he was a strong family man, carrying his home with him. The larger the volume of his accommodation, however, the smaller the cargo space remaining on his vessel, and thus the smaller the profit from his excursions.

The narrow-boat cabin is small. To the uninitiated it must seem impossibly small. Its dimensions are usually 10 feet long by 6½ feet wide and 5½ feet high. It provides the family's domestic quarters and, for the boatman, both his cradle and his deathbed. There is always a stove, a universal cupboard (whose door is hinged horizontally, folding down to form the table), and one bench/bed for

Illustrations from George Smith's *Our Canal Population*, published in 1875

the children; should the number of these reach large proportions, as it often did, then the surplus would sleep in a very small cabin built into the bows of the boat.

The origin of the boating families is not known. It has been suggested that they are of Romany stock and, certainly, the boat cabin with its decorations of lace, polished brass and brightly painted hearts, roses and castles has some visual affinity with the horse-drawn caravan. Canal trading was first established on the short water routes by boats without cabins, similar to the present 'day boats' of the Birmingham Canal Navigations, and it was not until longer routes were opened up that some sleeping accommodation was needed by the steerer.

Once established, the families became, and remain, very close-knit. They seldom married 'off the land' and, according to George Smith, inbreeding was not uncommon. Everyone 'on the cut' knew everyone else, no matter in which part of the system their trading was normally carried on. Amongst themselves they were freely communicative; to the outside world, however, they presented a separate, almost defiant face – a further reason for the intrusion of George Smith and a strong motive for their resentment of him.

George Smith's attitude and actions were not completely unjustified; there was, indeed, squalor and misery, as there

seems to be in every community. But, as he himself agreed, this state was most frequent among the 'Rodney Boatmen' – those not truly descended from boating generations, but who were trying to adapt to canal life after a landward upbringing.

The wildly publicised campaigns of George Smith were successful and a Canal Boats Act was passed in 1877. This left him free to meddle in the affairs of fairground people – a venture which proved rather a failure when they formed in their defence the United Kingdom Van-Dwellers' Protection Association.

The purpose of the Canal Boats Act was to prevent overcrowding and the spread of disease. The registration, marking and numbering of all boats, barges and floats became compulsory, as did regular inspections. The Act undoubtedly provided for healthier conditions in the boat cabins of those less careful of such matters. But George Smith was not one to rest on his laurels, for only days after the passing of the Act he had published '. . . a few observations and suggestions which, in my humble opinion, will

Opposite page The boat cabin of a horse-drawn narrow boat. It was common practice, on the death of a well-loved canal horse, to attach its tail to the tiller. Roses and castles, as seen in the pictures on the doors, are traditional features of canal boat decoration

Narrow boats of the past: horse drawn boats of the Bath and Bristol Steam Boat Company on the Kennet and Avon Canal, about 1880

go very far towards making this Act one of the most bene-ficient and popular that has been passed for some time'. An extract is here quoted:

The Paintings of the Numbers and other Marks . . . The name of the owner of the boat should be painted in letters, on both sides of the boat, of not less than 4 in. deep, the address in letters of not less than 3 in. deep. The name and address of the master or captain in letters of not less than 3 in. deep, but on a loose plate in the place where the name of the boat as a

rule now is. The initials, number, or other marks of not less than 3 in. deep, in a space of not less than 12 in. square, the letters to be red on a white ground. The process should be done by stencilling, and carried out in the presence of the sanitary inspector; for which purpose he should keep in his office a stencilling plate, with movable figures.

As for the bright paintings which adorn both inside and outside faces of the traditional narrow boat, colourful decoration of this kind has a valid precedent in Britain.

A narrow boat of today, on the Grand
Union Canal

Traditional decoration on a mule-
drawn boat

Farm carts and wagons were often embellished with distinctive liveries, scrolls and ornamental lettering, as much for delight as for advertisement. The art was revived in the house style boat-dressings of the great carrying companies – and almost died with them.

Roses and castles have more obscure origins. Possibly the flower emblems reflect a wish for, or memory of, a garden, while the castles might just be fanciful interpretations of wayside scenes in happy contrast to some of the true surroundings of early industrialism. There are some, again, who can find traces of gipsy ancestry in the art, but with no great foundation. After all, what could be more English than a rose – and what more impregnable than the boatman's own untaught philosophy of simplicity,

so well expressed by his own way of life and through the symbols of his art?

The canal company's employee was housed in a manner more conventional than that of the canal carrier. His status was just a little higher than the contemporary agricultural labourer, and his dwelling was usually of the same uncompromisingly simple style. The canal cottage seldom reflected any (often bizarre) current expression of architecture. Seldom, in fact, was it the product of an architect's genius. As with all canal buildings, the cottage was considered purely a utilitarian structure; its function was to accommodate an essential piece of canal machinery.

Every rule, and each generalisation, has its exceptions, and there are canal buildings which have neither style nor

Boat painters in Gas Street Basin, Birmingham, from an original painting by D. C. Miller

Working boatwoman: the late Mrs Bray at the tiller of her butty *Raymond* on the Grand Union coal run, late 1960s

Diversity of styles on the Grand
Union Canal over the short stretch
between Berkhamsted and Bletchley

simplicity. Exceptions, however, they are, for while the
curiosities are recorded, far greater numbers of more
commonplace buildings are neglected.

The construction of a canal was the sole concern of its
own company of proprietors and there was little uniformity
over the system as a whole as its parts grew together. A
lesson should have been learnt from this by the later railway
generations, particularly from the disadvantages of not
standardising track gauge. What there was of architectural
style on each waterway depended primarily on the background of the individual company engineer. Sometimes,
as with Telford, he happened to be an architect by profession. The principal occupation of the engineer, however,
was the surveying and surmounting of natural obstacles,
and mundane tasks such as cottage design were usually
passed down to assistants, the contractor, or perhaps the
local mason involved. Local craftsmanship, local materials
and local conditions were mainly responsible for the
appearance of these less significant of canal edifices.

It is the curiosities, such as the Thames and Severn

Somerton Deep Lock on the Oxford Canal

An uncompromising piece of design at the junction of the Welsh Canal and Prees Branch

Above Refined styling by Telford, on his Shropshire Union Canal
Opposite A Thames and Severn Canal circular cottage built of Cotswold stone, near Stroud

round tower lock houses, and the barrel-vault roofs on the Stratford-upon-Avon Canal cottages, that show the elements, if not the logic, of conscious design. The theory that all lock cottages were built 'upside-down' – with living quarters on the top floor, so that the keeper could more easily see boats approaching and prepare the lock – is suspect although, certainly, examples built in this manner have existed. At Tewkesbury Lock on the Lower Avon Navigation a modern cottage has the peculiarity of being built on *piloti* four feet above the ground level as a precaution against floods. 'Worcester. Tewkesbury and Gloucester would be inundated', claim the architects, 'before water enters these premises!'

However, it is not eccentricity that makes for attractiveness in any building. It is the unpretentious that has been successful on the English canal system, such as Telford's almost universal employment of shallow-pitched roofs with widely overhanging eaves, and the indication of

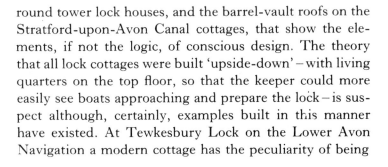

The canal in the town: Regent's Canal looking towards Maida Hill Tunnel, London, in the 1930s. A 'Josher', or Fellows, Morton & Clayton motor boat appears to be assisting in the movement of dockland lighters

architectural classicism exemplified by the handsome Regency bridge-men's cottages of the Gloucester and Berkeley Canal.

Canal-side building is by no means confined to dwellings, although the classifications may be applied to most structures that have their origins in the development of inland navigation – Navigation Offices, toll-houses, inns and taverns. The latter, which cater for thirsty travellers of every mode and in every age, may be found most often where a turnpike road has been intersected by the new cut; the public house can turn its face to whichever form of transport has the fortunes of the day. True canal inns were like 'The Tunnel' at Sapperton, which has survived its canal, or those almost ancient establishments on the banks of the Severn, said to be set apart at distances equivalent to one day's bow-hauling.

Concentrations of canal-side dwellings, particularly at major intersections, evolved inevitably into townships. As in all such new towns of the canal era, the community of Shardlow, on the Trent and Mersey Canal, existed purely to ensure an efficient interchange of goods between two waterways, a service upon which the economy of an industrial nation was to be founded. The waterways were the working centres of such towns, while the inns beside them were the retreats of boatmen and the focal point of their social life. Beyond the inns, warehouses, wharves and repair yards were scatterings of houses and cottages giving shelter to the people who worked there. Beyond these, too,

Warehouse at Glasson Dock on the Lancaster Canal, 1897. This example has the sophistication of internal loading bays

A warehouse at Shardlow, showing
the three-tiered loading platform

Another warehouse at Shardlow,
built in 1799

Above and opposite Brindley's canal 'new town' of Stourport-on-Severn in Worcestershire, at the junction of his Staffordshire and Worcestershire Canal with the River Severn

were the fields of farms, old and new, which, again with the help of canals, had to feed the ever increasing population. Although these towns at first lacked industry of their own they were an essential part of a complete industrial community; even those, like Shardlow, which remained agricultural, because they were now served by waterways were able to send food to the growing urban centres.

Brindley's work created another canal town of equal importance and greater notoriety – Stourport-on-Severn, in Worcestershire. Most impressive of all canal towns, however, and that most worthy of study, is Ellesmere Port, the one remaining 'new town' of the eighteenth century which still relies on water transport for its economy.

Most communities have too ancient a history for their origins to be traced completely. Ellesmere Port is an exception: it was founded on 1st July 1795, when the Wirral line

Ellesmere Port: the way to Ellesmere Port along Telford's old Wirral line, in 1967

Old Whitby Locks: the inn on the left was one of the earliest buildings at Ellesmere Port

of Telford's Ellesmere and Chester Canal came into use.

Previously the locality of the terminus at Netherpool was uninhabited. An early Elizabethan manor house, Pool Hall, existed about half a mile to the east, while a few farms were worked at Whitby, a mile inland. Marshes extended about two miles southwards, across which there was no road; the nearest main highway was the Chester-Birkenhead turnpike. Maps of 1819, 1829 and 1831 show that the settlement at Ellesmere Port remained isolated from other villages, its only link being by water.

The first residents of the junction area were lengthmen, a clerk, lock-keepers and, very shortly, an inn-keeper. The *Liverpool General Advertiser* of 30th July 1795 contains the following entry:

CAPITAL INN AND TAVERN. To be LET and entered upon immediately, neatly fitted up for the reception of company at Ellesmere Port – with suitable apartments for the accommodation of sea bathers and other conveniences, which considering the daily communication between Chester and Liverpool by the packet boats, make this situation desirable to any person of a proper capital and abilities for conducting an inn frequented by bathers and other genteel company and by persons in general navigating vessels upon the canal, or going by the Ellesmere boats and packets which change passengers and luggage at that place every day . . . . for a term of 7 years to a proper Tenant of good character and capital – and it is hoped none other will apply.

The community was at first known popularly as Whitby Locks, although as far as the Ellesmere Canal Company was concerned, from 1795 it was called Ellesmere Port, for it was the terminus of the canal linking Ellesmere in Shropshire with the River Mersey. Charles Hadfield records that the railway station was called Whitby Locks when it was opened in 1863, and that as late as 1921 traffic shipped to Ellesmere Port from Old Quay Dock, Liverpool, was known as 'locks goods'.

At the beginning of the nineteenth century the population of the town began to increase steadily. The whole area covered by the Port today provided dwellings for an estimated 120 people in 1720; 80 years later this had been swelled by only 50, but the 1851 census indicates a populace of 910, a reasonable influx for the time, to a town not founded on any industry.

There was a profitable passage of human cargo through the 'Locks', as advertisements in contemporary journals show. Passenger travel by canal could rival the stage coaches for both speed and comfort. Drawn by a pair of horses, the packet boat could quite often average between ten and twelve miles per hour, and the Birmingham-Wolverhampton packet boats claimed cabins 'heated in winter by pipes of hot water'. Each of the Ellesmere passenger boats could carry up to 200 passengers, and it is said that in the first month of service a total of 1700 were

Aerial view of the Canal Estate at Ellesmere Port, 1924

Ellesmere Port

carried. The packet boats on this route seem to have kept
running until the Birkenhead Railway was opened in 1840.

By 1800, Ellesmere Port was still little more than a tidal
basin and a set of locks between river and canal, but in this
year Telford reported to William Jessop, his principal, on
the state of the docks and discussed a possible extension of
the canal up the shore of the Mersey. Had this suggestion
been implemented, Ellesmere Port would have developed
no further as a trans-shipping point.

By 1828 trade was increasing, with imports of ores and
china clay, and exports of pottery and china goods. Telford
was ordered to carry out extensive alterations and additions
to the warehouses and docks as the only facility then existing was a small warehouse now known as the Grain
Warehouse. Telford planned the complete basin layouts
as they now survive, and in 1830 work was begun on the
project. In 1833 he reported that 'the extensive system of
warehouses and basins will be ready in three months for
operation. They offer complete accommodation for trans-
shipping both from the river and from the canal, and there
is plenty of space in the warehouses for storing articles of
all descriptions.'

The General Warehouse at Ellesmere Port was perhaps
the finest of all Britain's inland waterway structures.
Fittingly, it was one of the last of Telford's works to be
completed, although he did not live to see it. Even when
derelict, the elegance of its functional simplicity was not
extinguished. The very massiveness of the great arches

Telford's great warehouses at Ellesmere Port,
destroyed by fire in 1970. The boats were
unloaded directly beneath the arches, in the
soffit of which were set trap-doors through
which the cargo was lifted

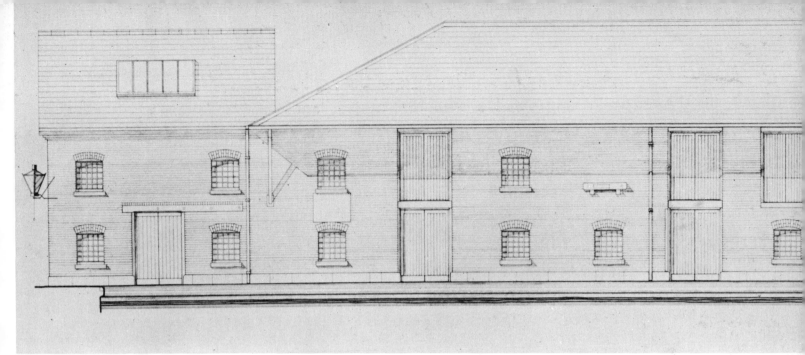

Elevations of Telford's warehouses

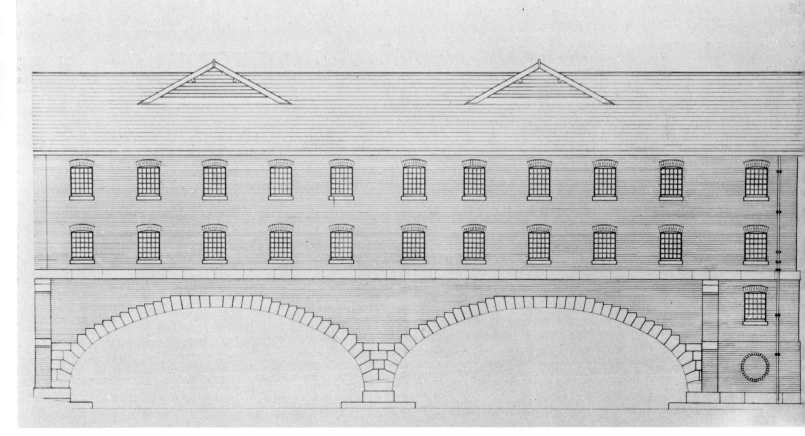

Ellesmere Port

upon which it stood and beneath which boats and cargoes from all parts of England passed and returned imparted a deceptive air of monumental permanence. The warehouse was totally destroyed by fire in 1970.

Of the complex as a whole, Telford's successor, William Cubitt, makes report:

With respect to Ellesmere Port, although I had heard something of the works erecting there, I was not prepared to see such as I found there and which I deemed to be of the highest order both of engineering skill in the design and of practical skill in the execution . . . . The warehouses for storing and wharfs on different levels for loading, unloading and transferring goods and cargoes are admirable and certainly the most complete I have seen . . . . I know of no place possessing so many advantages relative to the sea and inland navigation in so small a space and at so moderate a cost as these have been obtained.

Railway competition, and the resulting general decline

in canal trading, was to have a numbing effect on towns which had evolved in a manner similar to Ellesmere Port. With Stourport and Shardlow, in particular, there was to be almost a reversal of the events which had led to their establishment. Not that those communities, once established, followed completely the decline of their waterways; light industry on the one hand and a re-establishment of an agrarian economy on the other have assured, in each case, a leisurely survival. The story of Ellesmere Port continues to be exceptional.

In 1845–6, the Ellesmere and Chester, Montgomeryshire, Shrewsbury, and Birmingham and Liverpool Junction Canals combined to form the Shropshire Union Railways and Canals Company, with powers to build railways or to convert canals into railways. In 1847 the Shropshire Union was leased in perpetuity to the London and North-Western Railway, which actively promoted canal trade where it ran through the territory of the rival Great Western Railway. Whereas by the end of the nineteenth century many canals were in a poor commercial state, the Shropshire Union at Ellesmere Port was still very much alive according to the *Shipping World*:

. . . duplicate locks, wide and narrow, lead into big basins where little steamers and sea-going vessels lay loading and discharging. Among warehouses, cranes and brick heaps on the wharfs are a hydraulic generating engine and a pumping engine. Below is the big dock basin. . . . Enormous quantities of flint come up by sea from the south of England to be carried up to

Ellesmere, the centre of the Shropshire dairy industry

The maintenance yard at Ellesmere

Maintenance yard at Fradley, Trent and Mersey Canal

the potteries by canal, drain pipes for export to South Africa and Japan come back in great bulk; twelve months ago the quays were crowded out with them.

In 1894 came the Manchester Ship Canal, spreading the suburbs of that city along the line of its banks and bringing with it yet another era of prosperity for Ellesmere Port. The town continues to prosper today as a canal port. From the 1851 census (910), the populace increased to 4082 by 1901, and had exploded to 51,140 in 1966. Unlike the Severn and the Trent, the Mersey and its estuary seem destined for continued industrial exploitation; this is surely due in no small part to its inherent transport systems, past and present.

In the 1850s Ellesmere Port supported brick and tile works, a soap works, brewery and cement works. A gas works was established in 1863, and the Diamond Oil Company set up business in 1870. A century later oil refinery and distribution is still a principal industry, to-gether with motor-car manufacturing, chemical works and paper making, all of which use water transport. But today it is only the Manchester Ship Canal that gives the Port its economic life.

The mid-twentieth century traveller who approached this great canal centre by way of Telford's Wirral line saw little clear water. The way to Ellesmere Port was through a choking crust of weed and an ever-thickening mass of rubbish straying south towards Chester. The towpath, sometimes alive with bramble, now and then vanished into the substance of its waterway. An occasional boat penetrated this decaying greenness to find old Whitby Locks, the cottages, the inn with Telford's canal estate beyond, all just as it was more than a century before.

What of those communities whose established growth was interrupted by the coming of a canal era? Villages were little affected; Braunston, junction of four major canal routes, is an ever busy commercial and pleasure nucleus,

Right and below The Potteries seen from the Trent and Mersey Canal

Opposite The Shropshire Union Canal as it passes through Chester

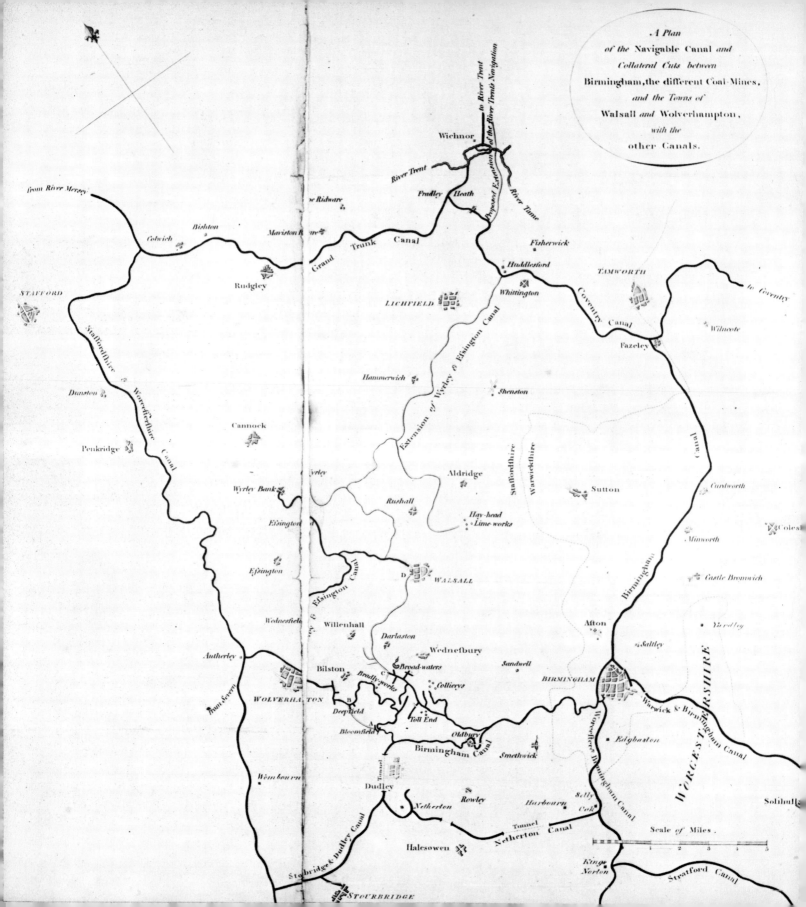

A Plan
of the Navigable Canal and
Collateral Cuts between
Birmingham, the different Coal-Mines,
and the Towns of
Walsall and Wolverhampton,
with the
other Canals.

Left Birmingham Canal Navigations –
a map of 1814
Right Canals in Birmingham

yet the village itself, set on the slopes above, remains quietly isolated from all this activity. Stoke Bruerne, interchange point between boats and tramway wagons while Blisworth Tunnel was building, and later a favourite halt for boatmen to view and purvey their painted ware, now has a museum and the waterside inn is a notable tourist attraction; but the village is undisturbed and unconcerned.

So the pattern is followed through towns and villages remarkable more for the poetry of their names than for past distinction: Husbands Bosworth, Market Harborough, Wheaton Aston and Fenny Compton – each uncommunicative in its somnolence with the water thoroughfares passing by.

Ironically, it is the canal which makes its way secret through older townships, almost unwilling to intrude upon their historic sanctity, with the result that its presence, and its potential, has in recent times been forgotten. This situation the canal brought upon itself by making possible cheap transportation of building materials hitherto alien to the districts. Towns expanded rapidly and factories, warehouses, even terraces of houses were brought to the very brink of the waterway. Shops, anxious to take full advantage of these new concentrations of population, crowded eagerly along both sides of every street.

Until very recently it was possible to travel right through the centre of Birmingham by water without seeing, or being seen by, a single one of its million inhabitants. The way was by ribbons of interlaced canal cutting, darkened

Left A dry dock on the Trent and Mersey Canal near Preston Brook

A dry dock on the Grand Union Canal near Tring, Hertfordshire

British Waterways depot at Bulborne, formerly the Grand Junction Canal Company's Works

The canal and the town: the Trent and Mersey Canal as it approaches Middlewich

passages of blank walls – unnoticed and unknown through man-made canyons and tunnels, piercing cellars all the way from Oozells Street to Spon Lane, from Pudding Green Junction to Black Delph Sluice.

There is a new relationship between canal and town in the Birmingham of today. Amenity is the all-important exigency of town planners, and 'linear water parks' are now providing recreational open spaces in the midst of tightly packed twentieth-century towns.

Birmingham has 120 miles of navigation, and, although many have been classed as 'remainder' waterways with uncertain future, it is gratifying that the city still supports water-borne commerce. The Salvage Department uses horse-drawn day-boats, while Gas Street Basin, once the scene of curious trans-shipments across the 'Worcester Bar' which physically separated the old Birmingham and Worcester & Birmingham Canals, is the headquarters of a young carrying company.

7

THE SECOND CANAL AGE

In almost every country where inland waterways had been a major transport system, the evolution of canals and their associated structures was interrupted by a 'railway mania'. By the time the railways were established and the mobile steam engine had become less than a novelty, there could be little doubt in the minds of investors of its potential value for moving large numbers of people at great speeds (initially for their entertainment), but it was not considered at first as a rival to canal traffic for heavy transportation. In fact, in its early development, there was even dispute as to its advantages over the stage-coach or packet boat for passenger transport.

Mid-nineteenth century England had a proved profession of civil engineers; the incredulity and mistrust towards them of the previous century had been confounded by the success of an extensive and valuable waterways system. When the engineers turned to the railways the further development of the canals was neglected. For many years all the great names in engineering, led by Stephenson and Brunel, were to be connected with railway development. Had but a fraction of their number been inclined to the furtherance of the country's now static inland navigations, commercial activity on England's present-day canal system might be a little less restrained.

Horses continued to be the principal form of traction on canals well into the 1920s, yet steam power had been tried, and proved, as early as the 1790s. It was to be perfected, not in a boat, but in a land-bound locomotive.

Canal boat lift at Fontinettes, France, shortly after its opening in 1888
Opposite Peterborough hydraulic lift on the Trent Canal System, Canada

The one physical factor which was to cause the decline of English canals was their inherent narrowness. Canal proprietors were afraid that the wash caused by screw propulsion would damage the banks of their restricted channels and the loads carried by a single narrow boat were minimal enough to be seriously reduced by the introduction of an engine into the valuable cargo space. In 1826 a boat with a stern paddle-wheel navigated successfully from London to Birmingham, but it carried only 20 tons.

In Brindley's time, lack of experience in establishing water supplies and in overcoming natural geography resulted in narrow canals. Later, the building of the Leeds and Liverpool and Kennet and Avon Canals, two broad intercoastal waterways, had shown that wide canals were feasible and workable, although naturally most econom-ically workable by wide boats, or breasted pairs of narrow boats. Problems of water supply on the latter navigation had been overcome simply; in one case a waterwheel lifted water from the very stream that was turning it, while at Crofton pumps were powered by beam engines. If this much could be achieved in the time of Rennie, the only barrier to the widening and improving of the whole system was really the existence of the railways.

This of course applied only to England, the first country to achieve a comprehensive and efficient railway system. Elsewhere contemporary engineers were still concentrating on improvements to their navigations. For this there was a logical reason, for the Continental waterways were, from the beginning, planned to larger dimensions (single barge-loads were thought of in hundreds of tons), and there-

Left A specially designed tractor for
hauling barges and lighters, on the lower
reaches of the Grand Union Canal

fore railways offered little real competition. But in England railways could, and soon did, offer attractive services to producers and manufacturers.

This did not mean that there was any sudden cessation of canal traffic in England. In proportion to the capacity of the system, tonnages carried up to the close of the nineteenth century were still considerable. Those canals that could not hold their own were themselves often the products of an earlier 'canal mania', canal building for its own sake rather than as a secure economic proposition.

There was also the problem of neglect. The railways, while openly desiring some of the traffic of canals, realised that their own capacities were also limited, and therefore had no desire for the canals' function to cease. Thus it might well have been for its own safety that a canal route came into railway ownership. But it is understandable that, in times of financial difficulty, it would be the railway undertaking of such a partnership which was supported, while the canal was allowed to decline.

While these developments were taking place, experiments were under way elsewhere to find alternative methods of haulage, literally by mechanising the horse. In France a steam tractor was tried in 1873, being guided by rails on the towpath, but having its traction against the path surface. A further attempt to use steam was made a few years later, again in France, but both were abandoned eventually because of opposition, physically, from the horses which were still in a majority on the paths and also

from the hauliers themselves. However, electricity was to become the saviour of bank haulage systems. Once again the earliest experiments were in France where, in the 1890s, three-wheeled electric tractors receiving their supply from overhead wires plied the banks of the Burgundy Canal. The chief merit of this system was that its power came from a dynamo driven by the waters of the upper reaches of the canal.

It was not long before this idea spread to America, where it was put to use on the Erie Canal. There the locomotive ran on a 'monorail' about four feet above the ground, and the sideways pull which is inherent with bank haulage was balanced out. But France is the only country which seems to have developed this method of traction on any sort of scale and there are now some 1000 kilometres of canals using electric haulage. Where traffic is heavy, both banks are often used, the tractors working in opposite directions. On single-line working, tractors meet, exchange tows, and proceed back over their own sections of track.

In 1888, towing by steam locomotives was carried out in England on about a mile of what is now the Middlewich branch of the Shropshire Union Canal. A speed of seven mph was reached by a locomotive pulling up to eight loaded boats. Although seemingly successful, the project came to nothing. In the present century, direct electric propulsion was tried on the River Wey: barges were equipped with motors receiving power from overhead lines. The results of the experiment were notable enough to produce a scheme

A traditional 'pair' of *motor* and *butty* moored against warehouses at Camden, Regent's Canal, London

for a 250-ton barge canal from the Thames at Ditton, through Guildford, Godalming and Alton, to Southampton. It was proposed that there should be three generating stations, providing the current to motivate the barges and to light the entire waterway. It was estimated that the cost of moving six fully-laden barges would be one-fiftieth of a penny per mile. Sadly, the Southampton Canal project failed to attract support. River Wey barges remained unpowered until their demise, and horses were employed until 1960, when their place was taken by tugs.

Apart from horse towing, which still survives, bank haulage in England is limited in the present day to the lower stretches of the Grand Union Canal, where small diesel tractors running on surfaced paths move lighters working from the Thames. But it was the oil engine mounted in the boat which, between the two World Wars, began to supersede the horses, and its advent gave convenience if little increase in speed. Thereafter, it was most usual for boats to work in pairs, one motor narrow boat towing a dumb 'butty'.

The most important signs of a new age of canals were connected not with the boats, but with the structures of the waterways themselves. The railways led to great advances in technical skills and, when opportunity arose, this was at last to be reflected in new works of heavy canal engineering.

In Britain, as elsewhere, the most important of such new works were designed to overcome extreme changes of level without the consumption of both time and water engendered by the use of conventional locks. As mentioned previously there were the early west country lifts and inclines, but these were on a scale only equal to the limited capabilities of their time, and usually they were simple alternatives to the pound lock passing only tub-boats. In the later part of the last century, and under the shadow of railway competition, the demand for canal efficiency led to the construction of devices capable of raising narrow boats and barges by means other than locks.

The first 'modern' engineering structure came into being on the Monkland Canal which ran for twelve miles between Woodhall and Glasgow. Although the history of inland navigation in Scotland is more truly connected with that of coastal navigation – the Caledonian and Forth and Clyde Canals were east – west routes for coasting vessels – there were five other canals conceived as independent navigations. The most profitable of these was the Monkland Canal.

Trade was principally downstream to Glasgow and thus the major part of the traffic passing up through the four pairs of staircase locks at Blackhill was empty. These locks were 66 feet long and 13 feet 6 inches wide, and raised the canal 96 feet. Being staircases, the amount of water used by these locks was considerable and, to pass only empty boats, excessive. Increasing trade over the canal more than a century ago brought with it such a severe shortage of water that, in 1849, it was decided to construct an inclined plane beside the locks to take the empty boats.

Blackhill Incline, built at a cost of £13,500, was opened in August 1850. It was 1040 feet long, and had a gradient of 1 in 10. The boats were moved, floating, in two tanks or caissons, each 70 feet long by 13 feet 4 inches wide, which ran on railways of 7-foot gauge. The motive power was supplied, through wire ropes 2 inches in diameter, by two stationary steam engines each of 25 hp. To navigate the locks took 45 minutes; to pass a boat up the incline took six. It is recorded that between 20th March and 23rd August 1851, 5227 boats were taken up the incline and 225 sent down it. It enjoyed heavy usage during the first sixteen years of its life and remained in operation until about 1887. In the locality it was known by the expressive title of the 'gazoon'.

The first and only large-scale inclined plane to be built on the English canal system was at Foxton, on what is now the Leicestershire branch of the Grand Union Canal. Opened in July 1900, at a cost of £39,224 including the purchase of land, the machine overcame a change in level

The experimental incline built by the Grand Junction Canal Company at their Bulborne works in 1896

of 75 feet. The promoters, the Grand Junction Canal Company, had undertaken elaborate methods of research by constructing a large-scale working model at their Bulborne works near Tring. The product of their experimentation was a concrete ramp over which two caissons passed, each 80 feet long by 15 feet wide by 5 feet deep, and capable of holding a 70-ton barge or two narrow boats, the one ascending counterbalancing the other descending. Power to overcome friction in the machinery was provided by a portable steam engine. Unlike the Blackhill Incline, that at Foxton had its caissons moving sideways, each having 8 sets of wheels running on 8 rails arranged in 4 pairs. At the lower end, the caissons were immersed in the canal to allow boats to enter and leave. The machinery evidently had its teething troubles, and there are rumours of pairs of boats, with their families aboard, being stranded for several days halfway up or down this unnatural concrete hill in

Leicestershire! The cost of running the incline in 1901 was £1 4s 6d a day, including coal, oil and labour. As an engineering structure the machine proved its worth, for the passage took only 12 minutes compared with $1\frac{1}{4}$ hours through the ten adjacent narrow locks. Economics, however, were against Foxton and the great increase in traffic from the Nottingham coalfields hoped for by the Grand Junction Company never materialised. Watford locks were rebuilt to their original narrow standard (not, as hoped, widened to permit a through barge route on the Leicester Line), and by 1910 the locks at Foxton had also been re-opened to normal traffic. The constant head of steam required could not be justified and, after intermittent working, the incline was dismantled in 1926 and its machinery sold two years later for a mere £250. Today, Foxton is a past wonder and even its few fragmented remains are difficult to identify.

GRAND JUNCTION CANAL
DETAIL OF THE "THOMAS" LIFT
AS CONSTRUCTED AT
FOXTON
SECTION A-A

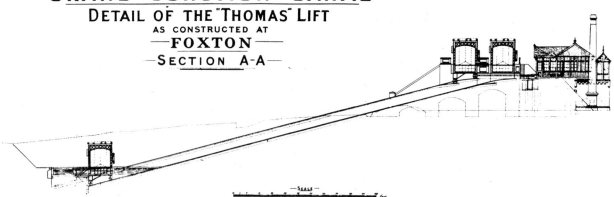

GRAND JUNCTION CANAL
DETAIL OF THE "THOMAS" LIFT
AS CONSTRUCTED AT
FOXTON
GENERAL PLAN

UPPER LEVEL

MOVABLE DOCK

POWER HOUSE

TAIL ROPE

HAULING ROPE

BALANCE ROPE

HAULING ROPE

MOVABLE DOCK

CATARACT CYLINDER

CATARACT CYLINDER

CATARACT CYLINDER

A

A

LOWER LEVEL

— SCALE —

Gordon Thomas | Engineers
James Thomas | 21 Surrey St. London WC

Above The Foxton Incline: the machine in operation in 1900
Right All that remains today of the Foxton Incline ramp

Still operating, however, and an equally impressive piece of engineering of yet earlier origin, is the one colossus of the abortive New Canal Age which the British system has retained, the Anderton Boat Lift. This was first constructed on the hydraulic lift principle in the 1870s. As the hydraulic lock is the type of lift still most frequently encountered on canal systems throughout the world a brief description of its operation might here be permitted.

In principle a hydraulic lock may be likened to two immense hydraulic lifts of the simple plunger type, having their presses filled with water and connected together so that the descent of the one causes the rise of the other. In place of the ordinary lift platform is a large watertight box (caisson) closed at each end by a gate. A lockage is performed by allowing a vessel to enter this chamber and then closing the open gates, one on the end of the chamber and the other at the end of the canal, thereby leaving the chamber independent of the reach and free to move vertically. The chamber and the vessel are then raised or lowered to the other reach. The chamber about to descend is loaded with a few inches more water than the other, thus giving it an additional load or surcharge which enables it to cause the ascent of the other when a valve on a pipeline connecting the two presses is opened.

The Engineer of 24th July 1908 contains the following description:

The Weaver is a river of only modest length, but it is navigable by steam barges of 300 tons burden for about 21 miles between Winsford, in Cheshire, and Weston Point, near Runcorn, on the Manchester Ship Canal, and thus serves to connect Northwich, the seat of the Cheshire salt and chemical industries, with the sea. In the early seventies [1870s] it was deemed necessary to provide facilities for intercommunication at Anderton between the Trent and Mersey Canal and the River Weaver, in order to save the expense and loss of time involved by the trans-shipment of goods passing from one to the other. The first means which suggested itself for this purpose was the raising and lowering of the vessels by a series of locks; but owing to the difference in the levels of the canal and the river at this point and the great space required for such a scheme, coupled with the delay which would be involved and the loss of water by the canal, the scheme was found impracticable. Mr (now Sir) Edward Leader Williams, who was at the time engineer to the Weaver Trust, conceived the idea of lifting and lowering vessels by hydraulic presses without taking any water from the canal. It should be pointed out that the canal, which for some miles runs parallel to the river, is on the top of a bank, while the river is below, the difference between the levels of the water being 50 feet 4 inches.

The lift was first built, to the principle described above, on an island of the Weaver. The works altogether com-

The Anderton Lift: as seen from the Trent and Mersey Canal

Opposite View of the structure from the River Weaver level

The Anderton Lift (*left*) view from the ascending caisson, (*above*) waiting to enter the aqueduct on the canal level

prised a basin opening into the canal; a wrought iron aqueduct 162 feet long and 34 feet wide built in three spans, to connect the canal to the lift; the hydraulic lift itself, on the island; and a new cut through the island from the lift pit to the main navigation channel of the river.

Of the lift itself each caisson was 75 feet long, 15 feet 6 inches wide, and held a depth of 5 feet of water. The total weight having to be moved in each case was 250 tons. Each trough was entirely supported and moved up and down by one central vertical ram 3 feet in diameter. At the corners of each of the troughs were cast-iron guide blocks running vertically in channels on the static lift structure. During operation, the difference in levels between the opposing caissons was 6 inches. At the bottom of the lift, as at Foxton, the descending caissons were lowered directly into the water. A watertight joint was needed at the top, however, between the raised caisson and the aqueduct. For this purpose the ends of the aqueduct and trough were bevelled, and a facing of timber was fitted on to the end of the trough, being correctly adjusted to the bevel of the face of the aqueduct. A 3-inch diameter round fillet of India-rubber was fixed on the face of the latter, and as an ascending trough was lifted the India-rubber was compressed between the two surfaces, making a watertight joint. After the joint was made, a valve was opened in the aqueduct gate to allow water to pass between it and the gate of the trough, and the aqueduct gate was lifted as soon as the water level was the same on both sides. The trough gate was pushed clear of the India-rubber fillet by the pressure of the extra 6 inches of water in the aqueduct, and could

A narrow boat entering the lift from the River Weaver level

Below left The top of the lift
Below A view along the aqueduct from canal level

therefore be lifted directly after the aqueduct gate. The water then flowed from the aqueduct to the trough until the level was the same, and the barges passed through. After the gates were closed, and the trough allowed to descend, the water between the gates fell through a pipe into the pit below, being lost to the river at each operation.

During the first ten years of working all went well, but then an accident occurred. One of the presses burst, and troughs, boats and families plunged to the bottom of the lift. Miraculously, the only injury was to the structure itself, the depth of water in the pit serving, no doubt, to cushion the blow. The fault was repaired, but it was then discovered that severe scoring of the metal surfaces was taking place within the rams. By 1896 this problem had become serious enough to warrant a detailed examination of the workings. It seemed that canal water, with which the cylinders of the presses were charged, was sufficiently impregnated with chemicals to set up an acute electrolytic action between the copper and iron of the rams. The trouble was temporarily checked by abandoning the use of canal water and installing a condensing plant to take the exhaust steam from the old engines used to provide auxiliary power. At the same time the aqueduct and trough gates were converted to electric operation, thus saving the labour of three men. In 1902 the steam engines and pumps were replaced by electric motors, with a subsequent reduction of working costs. Repair bills, however, were increasing, and the hydraulic system was becoming less efficient.

To renew the rams and presses at this time would have involved much expense but, also, the greater evil of a very long stoppage and therefore loss of income. The engineer to the River Weaver Navigation Trustees, Mr J A Saner, proposed that by abandoning the hydraulic system and converting the whole machine to electric operation, three separate stoppages of only two weeks each would be required.

This proposal was accepted and the converted lift, with its independently operating caissons slung from above and a new dry dock at the bottom, was opened in its present form in July 1908. The principal additions to the original structure, besides the running gear, are 252 tons of counter-balance weights hung against each caisson, divided into 36 groups of weights of 7 tons each. Eight horse-power only is required to overcome machine friction and provide motion, but a 30-hp motor is used, to allow for possible variations in water levels.

Whether by accident or by design, it is strange that the same ideas are often expressed simultaneously in entirely independent communities. Although one of the earliest large-scale canal lifts, Anderton has remained unique only in its own country. Similar and more sophisticated constructions are to be found in quantity in many parts of the world, but in particular on the great Continental and North American canal systems.

In the present age, structures have arisen which overshadow all these. One such is the Ronquières Incline

The scale of modern waterways construction:
Ronquières Incline, Belgium, completed 1968

on the improved route of the Charleroi–Brussels Canal, in Southern Belgium. Statistics reveal the magnitude of the project:

Length:	4650 feet
Lift:	221 feet
Capacity:	two 1350-ton vessels, or eight 350-ton barges
Operating time:	20 minutes
Construction period:	5 years
Costs:	in excess of £20 million.

In England the Manchester Ship Canal would have been an excellent testing-ground for techniques and inventions applicable to the modernising of the system as then existing, and the building of new, larger canals in Britain would have been in line with Continental development.

I sing a theme deserving praise, a theme of great renown, sir –
The Ship Canal in Manchester, that rich and thriving town, sir.
I mean to say it once was rich, ere these bad times came on, sir;
But good times will come back, you know, when these bad
    times are gone, sir!

The ballad was sung in 1827, at Manchester's Theatre Royal, but another 67 years were to pass before that city truly became a port.

The Ship Canal project, which finally occupied the years 1887 to 1894, was engineered by Sir E Leader Williams, the originator of the Anderton Lift and who,

therefore, can lay claim to be founder of a Second Canal Age in Britain. The progress of the work is too well documented, contemporarily and presently, to require any detailed examination here, but it is worth noting how great was the influence of the railway constructors on the machinery required to build the canal, and how great an influence, in turn, the canal was to exercise on the evolution of heavy engineering equipment.

More than 50 million cubic yards of material were excavated for the canal and its docks for which 98 steam excavators were employed. Over 170 locomotives with 6300 trucks and wagons were used to convey the material to spoil-grounds over the Engineer's 'macaroni route of 230 miles of railway, worming in and out, over and under, and alongside everywhere'. Amongst the excavators, 3 German and 4 French machines were used, but they worked best in soft materials and were not adapted for rough clearances. The English machines proved good all-rounders and could excavate an average of 700 cubic yards per day. Fifty-eight of these were 'Ruston & Dunbar Steam Navvies' made, confusingly, by Ruston & Proctor of Lincoln, being developed in an exemplary form for the canal works. These machines were motivated by 192 portable and other engines, and supplemented by the service of 212 steam pumps, 194 steam cranes, 59 pile engines, 200 horses and an army of nearly 17,000 individuals.

Two engineering features of this waterway are worthy of particular note. The first is the entrance lock at Eastham;

The construction of Eastham Lock, Manchester Ship Canal, during the 1890s

The ceremonial opening of the Manchester Ship Canal by Queen Victoria in 1894, showing the *Enchantress* leaving Trafford Wharf

The Manchester Ship Canal near Eastham

An aerial view of Salford Docks

Barton Swing Aqueduct showing a barge passing over the Bridgewater Canal
Below An aerial view of the Barton Swing Aqueduct

Barton Swing Aqueduct, pivoted to allow free passage of the Ship Canal

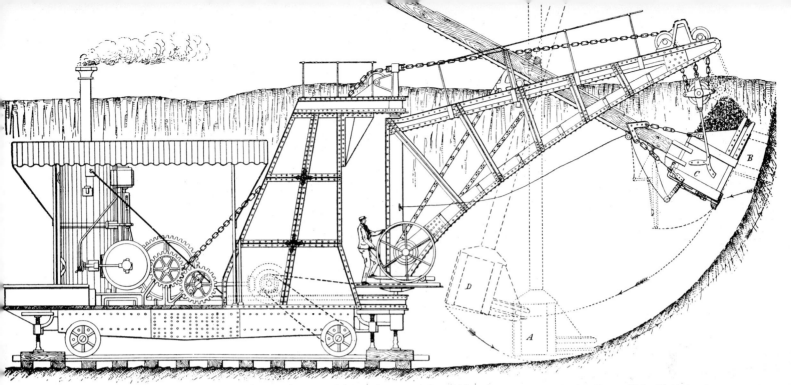

Ruston & Dunbar Steam Navvy – fifty-eight of these were used in the construction of the Manchester Ship Canal

at 600 feet long, 80 feet wide and 28 feet deep, it is the largest canal lock in Britain. Each gate weighs 300 tons.

The second, Barton Swing Aqueduct, is unique. The course of the Duke of Bridgewater's Canal is carried over its modern counterpart in a pivoting steel tank 235 feet long, 18 feet wide and 6 feet deep. The difference in level between the waterways is 26 feet, and when passage is required of the ship canal, the tank is swung clear on a central pier, bearing on 64 rollers. The aqueduct covers two cantilever spans of 90 feet, and is always swung full of water, the weight of the moving structure being 1400 tons. The method of obtaining seals between moving and static parts is based on that used at Anderton, except that the aqueduct has folding gates, where those of the lift are vertically rising to an overhead frame. It is an irony of unfulfilled symbolism that this modern example of functional ingenuity in canal work should replace Brindley's earliest, pioneering arches at Barton.

The Ship Canal project as a whole, while it should have raised interest and speculation in the modernising of earlier waterways, made but little impression. Possibly it was too much a project in splendid isolation, a concept far removed from what it was thought the canals could ever hope to become. Through it, one city became a prosperous port, but in contrast the rest of the canal system appeared inadequate and old-fashioned.

Not that the death-knell for small-scale inland navigations was being heard at all loudly at the beginning of the twentieth century; the Midland canals still had several decades of serious working life to add to their histories. It has been claimed that this part of the system was never more active than in the 1930s, and it has to be borne in mind that, until the Second World War, each canal company had to justify the not inconsiderable expense of maintaining its waterways in good condition, from an income derived mainly from tolls imposed on carriers. Although trading on the Midland canals was apparently good, statistics cannot tell the whole story, and more detailed investigation into the fortunes of some individual concerns belies such generalisations.

The Thames & Severn Canal underwent, according to its historian's colourful description, a 'death agony' lasting some 50 years between the 1880s and its final legal abandonment in 1933 (yet even now, in 1977, there are signs of a resurgence). During this time, it was controlled first by the Great Western Railway, then by a Trust comprising five navigation authorities and six public bodies, and finally, in what was later described as a 'daring adven-

Modern waterways construction: locks near Warwick on the London-Birmingham line of the Grand Union Canal being widened during the 1930s

ture into the realms of Municipal Socialism', it was taken over by the Gloucestershire County Council in 1901. This was far from being a foresighted involvement in amenity and recreation on the part of the Council, their action being economically motivated by an almost frenzied desire to prevent railway monopoly. Keeping the canal open was supposed to provide healthy competition to this end. In fact, the waterway was constantly plagued by a leaking summit level and by inaccurate engineers' reports. During this latter period, the Thames & Severn was actually subsidised, largely from public funds, to the extent of £64,000.

The later life of the London to Birmingham line has an equally complex history. The Grand Union Canal Company came into existence on 1st January, 1929, unifying control of the old Grand Junction, the Regent's, the Warwick Canals and, in 1931, of the Leicester Canal and the Erewash. This vast concern, which also operated its own carrying company, began a series of ambitious projects. Financed in part by the Government as a means to combat the Depression nearly £1,000,000 was spent on general improvements to its canals in particular the construction of 51 new broad locks between Calcutt and Sampson Road. The intention was that the London–Birmingham main line should ultimately be navigable by 12ft 6in-wide barges carrying 66 tons. Although this was never realised, one such boat, the *Progress*, was built and tried experimentally. The widening of the locks, did however, make it possible for pairs of narrow-boats to work through breasted-up on many stretches, thus increasing the efficiency of the waterway to existing carriers.

Between 1934 and 1937, the Grand Union Canal Carrying Company expanded its fleet from 12 to 186 pairs of boats. To keep them in work, it had to undercut other carriers; the consequent general lowering of tonnage rates leading to a decline in the standard of living of the working boatmen.

None of this attempted expansion was supported by a notable increase in trading and towards the middle of the twentieth century, the condition of the system was probably at its worst and the outlook at its gloomiest. In 1946 the Inland Waterways Association was founded as a non-profit distributing company; of its activities the most basic and most important has been to inform the public of the existence of their inland navigations, which has resulted in many canals being saved from extinction. All

The mechanical handling equipment at Ferrybridge

who care about Britain's waterways owe an inestimable debt to the Association and its founder, Robert Aickman.

On 1st January, 1948 the era of private ownership for most waterways came to an end. Many navigations which had been under national control during the war, as well as all railway-owned canals were nationalised under the British Transport Commission. Since 1963 this nationalised system has been under the authority of the British Waterways Board, appointed originally by the Minister of Transport and latterly by the Minister for the Environment. The Board controls 1900 miles of inland navigations. In spite of immense potential, less than 2% of all Britain's internal freight is moved on them.

The Transport Act of 1968, while taking away the public's right of navigation, promised retention of most of the system at least for use by pleasure craft. Commercial traffic may still use any of the designated cruising waterways, but scheduled maintenance standards, particularly depths proposed for dredging, would seem to preclude their serious working by carriers. As canal areas and basins are filled in to provide new car parks and extra storage space, canal-side industry expands its fleet of lorries and vans. How long can Britain's canals survive in the half-romantic haze of pleasure cruisers and decorated working boats?

Concerned with areas of open country rather than with

A barge tippler at the Central Electricity Generating Board's station at Ferrybridge in Yorkshire, designed by Strachan & Henshaw of Bristol. Special barges are used, each of 210 tons, being propelled by a tug in trains of three. The tippler lifts the barges 40 feet out of the water and discharges their contents into an elevated receiving hopper, which in turn feeds the conveyor system leading to the power station. The total time for unloading is nine minutes, giving an unloading rate of 1,000 tons per hour

Part of the unloading cycle of the barge tippler at Ferrybridge

A narrow-boat graveyard at Braunston

canals in any specific way, the National Parks and Access to the Countryside Act of 1949, dealt for the first time with public authority involvement in leisure activity on a large scale. There are canals linking all major centres of population to open countryside and, with the various canal elements opening up possibilities to walkers, anglers, boaters and naturalists, as well as to followers of industrial history, many long stretches can be seen as continuous 'linear country parks'. It took a generation for such recognition to become officially adopted policy, yet, in only a decade since the 1968 Act, the saturation point is within sight. With increasing personal wealth, and increased leisure time, more boats are owned. Exploration holidays aboard self-drive hire cruisers are popular. The irony is that, of all privately-owned inland pleasure craft 90% are idle for most of the year: a large, static investment in luxury.

If, indeed, it is pleasure craft alone that must take over the waterways, then much canal machinery and building will outlive its inherent functionalism. A simple architecture which has survived from that harsh age of industrial birth is assured an unwitting retention, if only to delight the water-borne tourist. But there are, even now, thriving commercial waterways in Britain, the operation and structure of which point out a new canal landscape, whose foundation must be one of heavy engineering.

8
THE NEW NAVVIES

'I'll go,' said I one day, 'where are no guides and scarce a map is printed. Who knows his way about the canals of England?'

'They begin at Regent's Park,' said a man.

'And then?' I asked him.

'There's one passes near Slough on the Great Western. I've seen it from the train.'

'If that's all that's known about them,' said I, 'I'll get a barge myself and go on till I stop.'

E. Temple Thurston, *The Flower of Gloster,* 1911

The time has passed for expansion, speculation and mania. The noise and excitement, perhaps the grime and squalor too, are gone with the commerce from warehouses, wharves and basins. Inland ports face away from their quays; wind pulls the thick surface of unused water. A time has come to stand back from that water's edge, to look at what is left of the first transport system of the industrial age, seeing what it has become, finding out its place in the contemporary patterns of life.

There were a few who travelled for pleasure, or to sate their curiosities, while the canals were still commercially active (their journals suggest that they avoided or ignored the activity). Those intrepid enough to overcome the administrative problem of obtaining various passes and permissions of several Canal Companies, Railway Companies and other owners or bodies, derived at least scenic satisfaction from their voyaging:

Congestion in Boulters Lock, Maidenhead, c. 1890. Although today the Thames can be equally busy at the height of the season, such a conglomeration of small unpowered craft would be unusual

. . . The water was cold and silky to the fingers as we dipped a decorated bowl into it from the stern of the Eve. Eyes refreshed and freed from the smoke of the paraffin, we could see beyond the village a tall thin church spire, a low valley side edged with trees, a rough skyline of cottages and a tower where another Fosse village stood. On this morning I envied the people of the narrow boats, who awake each morning to such surroundings.

Soon the sun lit the red wall of the farmhouse and poured over the meadows, where the dew lay heavy on dead thistle tops, ragwort and tufty grass. Cobwebs glistened between plant and ground; the smoke from the chimneys reddened, and all the water was sunlit and warm in colour. We loosed the ropes and paddled silently out of the pool, as two people might leave a church service before it was over, until we reached the opening: Once free of the weeds of the backwater, we broke every spell of the morning peace, startled fowl, water

rats and pigeons with the clatter of our backfiring gas engine, and rattled ahead to the lock-keeper's house, our minds fixed hungrily on breakfast. . . . (John O'Connor, *Canals, Barges and People,* 1950)

Pleasure cruising on this scale, amounting sometimes to slow but comfortably padded meanderings between good-class hotels, was a sport restricted until the present decades to the well-to-do. A leaflet of 1908 shows that it cost £1.10s to make one passage of the Thames & Severn Canal from Inglesham to Wallbridge with a 'Pleasure Boat or Steam Launch': tolls comparably higher for a single journey than a suitable proportion of the present day annual licence, which covers the whole nationalised system. But others could enjoy the amenity of the water-

An unlikely combination of river users shown in a Victorian sketch. The scene is on the Thames, which supported regular narrow-boat traffic until the 1930s

Picture postcards, probably Edwardian, showing boating stations on the Basingstoke Canal at South Camp and North Camp (Ash Vale), which were patronised largely by an army clientele from Aldershot. The latter establishment survives to the present day

ways in more limited fashion, with the expenditure of more energy. The Thames was well established as a boating arena at the height of Victoria's reign, while a canal such as the Basingstoke, always under-used by carriers, essentially rural in character, wide, adjoined by lakes and flashes, was ideal for the establishment of boat-houses for the hire of skiffs, punts, canoes and rowing craft large and small, particularly when the British Army built its home on the canal banks, providing these boating stations with an extended clientele.

Houseboats have multiplied as working boats declined, often a result of direct transfer from the one function to the other. Being static they have become elements of the canal environment, sometimes attractive, although seldom having the entire approval of local authority or health

Hay Incline, Shropshire Canal, Coalport, restored to working order as part of the Ironbridge Gorge Museum, 1976

inspector. Houseboats, skiffs and punts, walkers, anglers, bathers . . . all are valid users of the 'amenity waterway', but none require the retention of its specific function as a highway.

To close the navigation is a simple bureaucratic procedure (the public right to navigate was lost in 1968) but the water channel is less easily eliminated. In the first two decades of Nationalisation, perhaps the time of greatest threat of severance for many parts of the established system, enthusiasts frequently had to advance arguments to show the higher costs of complete elimination (piping and filling) as against maintenance of the navigation: although these comparisons did not always take into account the commercial value of land thus reclaimed

which, in urban areas, could have reached significant figures. As to the permanence of the way when left only to Nature, there survive many stretches of long-defunct canal which have the appearance of being as sound and as watertight as those still in work.

It is, perhaps, the pleasure seekers after all who have won the day. By emphasising the waterways' amenity potential and by pointing out that this can be best realised by keeping them open as navigations, public opinion and community reaction have been persuaded away from the idea of canalside as back-end-of-town-convenient-rubbish-tip-relic-of-a-past-age, towards pictures of recreational centres, linear parks and green-lined pathways into the countryside's heart. Valid thoughts, but the reality at

The western portal of Greywell Tunnel restored to its original form by its owner, Hampshire County Council, as a contribution to European Architectural Heritage Year, 1975

present is financial restriction, thus poor maintenance standards and frequently impenetrable towpaths which, with less-skilled users, result in less than efficient water highways.

This picture places commercial carrying in the background. The implementation of minimal dredging standards for shallow-drafted cruisers precludes the serious carrier from using 'cruiseways' (most of the Midland waterways), although freight handling had drastically declined long before the 1968 Transport Act introduced them. Narrowboat carrying has ebbed to the point of being kept nominally alive only by dedicated enthusiasts; another pleasure use of canals, in fact. At the fringes of the system freight carriage is healthier. In the North-east, a contemporary report claims that the Sheffield and South Yorkshire Navigation – a linked complex of canal and river serving Nottingham, Rotherham, Leeds, Goole and the Humber estuary – with a present capacity of 90-tonne barge loads, could be improved to accommodate 700-tonne loads for a capital cost of £3·8 million – a relatively slender sum in public expenditure terms, especially when the scheme's promoter, the British Waterways Board, can claim good user support for the improved waterways.

In the South, a project for widening the lower reaches of the Grand Union Canal to float off-loaded containers

Man power. Lock 26 on the Basingstoke Canal being restored by recruits employed under the Government's Job Creation Scheme, 1977

Steam power. Volunteers operating the Surrey and Hampshire Canal Society's 70-ton steam-powered dredger and attendant barge and tug on the Basingstoke Canal at Colt Hill, Odiham, 1977

direct from Dockland to an out-of-London distribution terminal at Watford has the full support of planning and navigation authorities but, like the previous example, still awaits financial backing.

The most active phenomenon of the late-twentieth century English canal system is restoration work. All aspects of canal building from towpath clearance to lock and lock-gate construction are carried out by single-minded volunteers from all social strata. This recreational, spare-time labour force performs with, over all the varied personal motives, the collective aim of rescuing from dereliction defunct and dying navigations. The standards of most restored waterways suggest that it is again pleasure traffic rather than commerce which is to be the principal future user but the most dedicated of the new navvies find more fulfilment in the work itself than in the leisure aspects of its product, and it might be that they would see little to interest them in an efficiently functioning, well-maintained navigation.

The restoration movement began in the 1950s, in the

Canal mania in the 1970s. The architectural features of Coates portal, Sapperton Tunnel, under restoration. The foundations of a scheme to re-open the Thames & Severn Canal have been laid, but expense may prove an obstacle; consultant engineers report that the cost of reinstating navigation through the tunnel alone could be £2 million

heart of England. First results were the Lower Avon, 7 locks, 26½ miles, reopened 1962; and the Stratford-upon-Avon Canal, 36 locks, 13¼ miles, reopened 1964. Since then, reconstruction projects have been or are being actively pursued on canals in places as far apart as Tiverton, Basingstoke, Stourbridge, Grantham and Pocklington, using tools and materials ancient and modern as wheelbarrows and hydraulic excavators. In fact, the present day sees a mania for projects almost rivalling the 'canal mania' of the late eighteenth century. Even vanished canals are being resurrected in intent under the pens of letter-writers and committee-oriented promoters.

The most important aspect of restoration work is the concern of the individuals for the detail of what they are re-creating. Whereas pleasure operators have neither the resources nor, perhaps, the inclination to care in a constructive way for the visual fabric of their waterways, the restorers make positive efforts to rebuild in the styles of the original or sympathetic to the character of the original works, thus ensuring the survival of functional elegance in a kind of architecture which embodies human endeavour and expresses human scale.

Completed restoration works on and beside the Coalport Branch of the Shropshire Tub Boat Canal, Ironbridge Gorge Museum site, 1976

APPENDICES

One of the Grand Junction Canal Company's steam tunnel tugs, 'Spider', introduced in 1871 to replace endless-wire-rope haulage through Blisworth and Braunston Tunnels. The boat is 49 ft long and has its engine and boiler mounted amidships. Steam haulage continued through these tunnels up to 1936

Canal Terminology

Perhaps the most comprehensive manual of information ever made available to canal users was *Bradshaw's Canals and Navigable Rivers of England and Wales,* last printed in 1928. This 'Handbook of Inland Navigation for Manufacturers, Merchants, Traders and others' was compiled by Henry Rodolph de Salis, chairman of Fellows, Morton and Clayton, canal carriers. De Salis travelled the whole waterways system in his specially built steam launch, *Dragonfly,* with the principal aim of finding trade for his company. He also recorded canal life as it was enacted in the days when most traffic was still horse-drawn. The following glossary of canal terminology is based largely on that contained in *Bradshaw,* with additions where necessary to bring the material up to date.

ANIMALS, a boatman's name for donkeys, which were frequently used for towing on canals adjacent to the River Severn; a pair would take the place of one horse.

BALANCE BEAM, the beam projecting from a lock gate, which balances its weight, and by pushing against which the gate is moved.

BANK SIDE, as opposed to TOWPATH SIDE, that side of the canal opposite the towpath.

BARGE, a term covering a variety of vessels, both sailing and non-sailing, in use for canal and river traffic, and whose beam is approximately twice that of a narrow boat. The term is often applied erroneously to all types of canal vessels.

BECK, a dyke or drain.

BOBBINS, short hollow wooden rollers, several of which are usually threaded on to each of the traces of horses engaged in towing, to prevent the traces chafing.

BOLINDER, one of the earliest diesel engines used to power narrow boats. An important advantage over the steam engine was the saving of five tons of cargo space. A disadvantage was that it had to be preheated with a blowlamp before starting. This engine was used on nearly all powered boats up to the 1930s.

BOSTOCKS, wooden blocks on which a boat rests in dry dock.

BOW HAULING, propulsion of boats by men hauling as distinct from the method of hauling by horses.

BREAST (of a lock gate), the vertical post of the gate furthest from its hanging.

BULK, the decorative deep curve at the front of a narrow boat, formed of canvas padded out with hay on wooden formers.

BUTTY, a boat working in company with, and towed by, a motor narrow boat.

BYE TRADER, any trader on a canal not operated by the canal company itself.

CHALICO, a mixture of tar, cow hair and horse dung made hot and used for caulking the seams of wooden canal boats.

CLOUGH, a northern colloquial term for paddle.

COMPARTMENT BOAT, commonly called a 'Tom Pudding', a type of boat in use on the Aire and Calder Navigation, which is worked in trains with other similar boats.

CRANK, see WINDLASS.

CRATCH, the support of the gang plank of a narrow boat located at the front end of the boat.

CUT, a boatman's term for a canal thus NARROW CUT denotes a narrow canal.

DAY BOATS, or OPEN BOATS, boats without accommodation, used to work short distances only.

DOORS, a Fen term for gates; in the Fens all lock gates are called Sluice Doors.

DRAW, to draw a paddle, slacker, slat, weir or staunch, is to open it in order to allow water to escape. The reverse is to lower, drop, shut in, or in the case of a staunch to set.

DYDLE, a Norfolk term, meaning to dredge, or to clean out.

EYE, Fen term for the opening closed by a paddle.

FEST ROPES, a pair of ropes attached one to each side of a Fen lighter, the loose ends being passed round the steering pole to steady it when in use.

FLASH, the body of accumulated water suddenly released and used for the purpose of assisting navigation on rivers.

FLASHERS, see PADDLE.

FLASH LOCK, see LOCK.

FLAT, a Mersey flat is the type of vessel which carried the bulk of the trade on that river and on neighbouring canals. A BLACK FLAT is a larger vessel for trading between Liverpool and the River Weaver.

FLEET, a Norfolk term for shallow.

FLY BOAT, a boat which worked through non-stop, day and night, on a particular freight route. Fly working was carried out on the Grand Union from London to Birmingham until 1939, when a rule was made that stop planks must be put down at certain places at night as a precaution against flooding, resulting from possible bomb damage.

FLY PADDLES, see PADDLE.

FRESHET, an increase in the flow of a river due to rain.

GALLEY BEAM, a beam linking across the top of the gate posts of a pair of old-fashioned river lock gates that were hung on hooks and rides. The galley served to keep the gate posts in place, and prevented them from falling inwards towards each other, which the weight of the lock gates would otherwise induce, this type of gate being wholly unbalanced.

GANG, a number of boats, particularly lighters, working together.

GANG PLANKS, removable planks used to afford a means of passing from one end of a narrow boat to the other over the top of the cargo space. Intermediate upright supports are called 'Stands'; these are detachable, fit into mortices in the stretchers and boat's floor, and have the gang planks tightly lashed down to them.

GAS BOATS, those boats operated by Thomas Clayton of Oldbury, and used to carry crude tar in the Birmingham area. The hold was decked over forming a tank and making the boat virtually unsinkable.

GATES (Lock-), the enclosing structure at either end of a Lock chamber, the components and method of construction being entirely traditional. Frames are first made whose uprights are 'heel posts' and the pivoting members, and 'head posts' (also 'mitre posts' on pairs of gates), are

An unusual 'collar' (see GATES)

A new gate for fitting on the Audlem Flight, Shropshire Union Canal. The 'heel post' is on the right-hand side, with a 'tan-pin' seated in it. The sluice hole and paddle-guides can be clearly seen on the top face of the gate (see GATES)

spaced by horizontal 'bars'. The gate tapers from its pivot; a heel of 12 by 10 inch oak will reduce to a head of 10 by 9 inch section. The gates are 'planked' on their top sides (toward the higher water level) with 9 by 2 inch section archangel, deal or oak. 'Balance beams' vary with age and origin, from unshaped and often mis-shapen tree trunks to second-hand telegraph posts. Heel posts are mounted on iron 'tan pins', which rotate in 'pots'. Iron 'collars' hold the heel posts upright, and are restrained by the masonry of the chamber. A heel post has a rounded face, and its bearing member, a 'hollow quoin', mounted in the lock side, is correspondingly concave in section. The lower gate members close against 'cills' set on the lock 'aprons', while the head posts are mitred together. Writing in 1838, the essayist Peter Barlow recommended that 19° 25′ is 'the angle at which a pair of lock gates should be situated so as to have the greatest strength'. The head posts of single gates close against 'clap quoins'.

GAUGING, the means of ascertaining by the draught of the vessel the weight of cargo on board for the purpose of taking tolls. The initial gauging of canal boats is carried out at a weigh dock, where particulars of the boat's draught are taken when empty, when fully loaded, and at intermediate points, during loading. Special weights are kept for this purpose, which are lifted in and out by cranes. The result arrived at is then either calibrated on graduated scales fixed to the boat's sides, which can be read at any time, or the particulars of each vessel are sent to every toll office, from which, on gauging the immersion of the boat the number of tons on board can at once be ascertained. On the Glamorganshire Canal at North Road Lock, Cardiff, boats were gauged in the first instance by being weighed, both empty and loaded, on a weighing machine. The boats to be weighed were floated into a dock over a large cradle, and water was let off until they rested upon it. The scale beam connected with the cradle was of much less length from the cradle to the fulcrum than from the fulcrum to the scale pan in which the weights were placed for reading the result, thus enabling those weights to be proportionally lighter than the actual dead weights. This machine is now preserved outside the Waterways Museum at Stoke Bruerne. A similar machine was once in use at Midford on the Somersetshire Coal Canal.

GONGOOZLER, an idle and inquisitive person who stands staring for prolonged periods at anything out of the common, particularly at canal boats and canal people.

GROUND PADDLES, see PADDLE.

HAIN, a Norfolk term for 'higher', particularly in relation to water levels.

HALING WAY, a Fen term for towpath.

HANDSPIKE, a tool used to raise early ratchet paddles.

HAULING PATH, another name for towpath.

HEEL POST, the vertical post of a lock gate nearest to its point of hanging, and the axis on which the gate turns, being rounded at the back to fit into the hollow quoin, which partially restrains it, see also GATES.

HOLD IN, and HOLD OUT, boatman's terms used as directions for steering; 'hold in' means hold the boat in to the towpath side of the canal, and 'hold out' means to hold the boat away from it.

HOLLOW QUOIN, the recess into which the heel post of a lock gate is fitted, and in which it revolves when being opened and closed.

HORSE BOAT, a small open boat for ferrying towing horses from one side of a river to the other, used in the Fens and neighbouring country on account of the long distances which would otherwise have to be travelled by the horse and driver to the nearest bridge.

HORSE MARINES, a Yorkshire term for men who contracted for the haulage of canal vessels by horses.

HOUSE LIGHTER, a Fen term for a lighter which was provided with a cabin.

INVERT, an inverted arch of brick or masonry, used to form the bottoms of locks and tunnels in cases where, owing to the nature of the soil, lateral or upward pressure had to be sustained.

JACK CLOUGH, see PADDLE.

JOSHER, a boat belonging to Fellows, Morton and Clayton Ltd the canal carriers: the christian name of Mr Fellows having been Joshua.

KEB, an iron rake used for fishing up coal or other articles from the bottom of a canal.

KEEL, a type of vessel once in extensive use on the rivers and canals of Yorkshire and district.

LEE BOARDS, boards used by sailing barges which can be lowered into the water or raised at will, for the purpose of decreasing the leeway made by the vessel when sailing close-hauled. These boards are fitted in pairs, one on each side of the vessel, and when in use act as a keel.

LEGGING, a method of propulsion through tunnels where professional leggers, strapped to special boards on the sides of a boat, would push on the sides of the tunnel and literally walk the boat through.

LENGTHMAN, a canal employee directed to regulate and maintain a particular length of canal; his principal task being to make sure the water level is kept constant by operating paddles and let-offs. In the days of horse-drawn traffic, he had also to keep the towpath clear.

LET-OFF, a device for getting rid of water from a canal, either when there is a danger of flooding, or in order to empty a reach for repair. The earliest kind was a self-sealing flap on the canal bed which was raised by a winch and chain. Modern patterns more closely resemble the lock paddles, and are located in the canal bank, being operated by a windlass.

LEVEL, the condition when two reaches of water, one on each side of a lock or weir, become level through the action of the tide or by other means.

LIGHTER, a term used to describe vessels on many navigations, including the Thames, the Fens, the River Stour (Suffolk), and the Bridgewater Canal.

LOCK, a device for overcoming changes of level in the navigation of rivers and canals, see also GATES. FLASH LOCK, also called STAUNCH or NAVIGATION WEIR, a single barrier across the navigation channel through which the flash is released from the higher to the lower level, thus permitting navigation between the two. POUND LOCK, consists of a chamber built generally of brick or masonry, and provided at both ends with a gate, or gates, and the necessary paddles or valves for controlling the ingress and egress of water. TO LOCK, to work a vessel through a lock.

LOODEL, a staff used to form the vertical extension of the tiller of a barge to facilitate steering when there are high loads such as hay or straw on board. The loodel when required is inserted in a mortice in the fore end of the tiller.

MITRE POST, where lock gates are in pairs, the two breasts are usually mitred to bed against each other when shut, and in this case are termed mitre posts.

MONKEY BOAT, a London term for Narrow Boat.

MOTOR BOAT, a narrow boat powered by an inboard diesel engine.

NARROW BOAT, the type of boat most commonly in use on canals in Great Britain, having a beam of about 6 feet 10 inches. Sometimes called a long boat, or just 'boat'.

NIP, a term unique to the River Trent meaning a narrow place.

NUMBER ONES, boats that are owned by the men who work them, and who consequently are their own masters, in distinction to boats owned by a company.

OVERLINE BRIDGE, a bridge that carries an alternative mode of transport over the line of the waterway, but allows passage beneath.

PACKET, a passenger-carrying canal boat: in their hey-day express packets were worked continuously by teams of horses and always had right of way over other working boats. Sometimes they were equipped with a sharp curved blade on the bow which would cut through the towing rope of any boat failing to move out of their path.

PADDLE, a form of sluice valve called SLACKER and CLOUGH in the North of England. The word CLOUGH, when used in the Fen country generally denotes the large shutter closing the navigation opening of a staunch. SLAT is the Fen term for paddle, hence SLATS and EYES, the eye being the opening closed by the slat. GROUND PADDLES, the paddles at the head of a lock that admit water by culverts or sluice-ways built in the ground as distinct from the paddles used in the lock gates. They are known as 'Jack Cloughs' on the Leeds and Liverpool Canal. Some of the locks on early canals have only ground paddles, but usually there are additional paddles fitted in the top gates which help to fill the lock quickly. In different localities, these are variously termed Fly Paddles, Ranters and Flashers.

PEN, or LOCK PEN, a Fen term meaning lock chamber.

TO PEN, a Fen term, meaning to work a vessel through a lock.

POUND, the stretch of water on a canal between two locks.

POUND LOCK, see LOCK.

PUDDLE, a water-tight lining of clay worked up with water and spread in layers on the bottom and sides of a canal, or reservoir, when excavated in porous strata.

PUNT, another name for a Thames lighter.

QUANT, a pole or shaft used for propelling a vessel, thus 'to quant', means to propel a vessel by means of a quant.

RAM'S HEAD, the wooden post to which the blade of the rudder is attached on a butty or horse-drawn narrow boat, and in which the tiller bar fits.

RANTERS, see PADDLE.

RATE, for canal carriage, the rate was the toll payable plus the haulage charge.

REACH, (of a river), the stretch of water between two locks.

RIMERS, in a navigation weir, the rimers are the removable posts which hold the stop planks.

RISERS, see STAIRCASE LOCKS.

RODNEY BOATMEN, the name given by George Smith, the politician and reformer, to the rougher class of boatmen who were born 'on the land', rather than being descended from generations of boatmen.

ROVING BRIDGE, or TURNOVER BRIDGE, a bridge carrying the towpath from one side of a canal to the other, alternatively over a branch or junction.

SCREW, a boatman's term for a vessel driven by a propeller.

SEIZING CHAIN, the chain by which two Fen lighters are fastened to each other, stem and stern, when forming part of a gang.

SET, to set a staunch is to close it in order to allow the water level to build up.

SHAFTING, the propelling of a vessel by means of a long shaft or pole, a method sometimes used in tunnels.

SIDE POND, a small reservoir beside a lock into which water can be discharged when emptying the lock, or from which water may be taken when filling it, thereby conserving most of the water. See also the chapter on locks.

SLACKER, see PADDLE.

SLAT, see PADDLE.

SLUICE, a Fen term for a lock.

SNATCHER, a short towing line from a narrow boat to a butty.

SNUBBER, a long towing line from a narrow boat to a butty.

SOAR PIN, see STUD.

SPILLWAY, an overflow for excess water beside the navigation channel, by means of which a maximum water level is imposed on the pounds and the risk of flooding reduced.

SPREAD or SPRIT, a Fen term for a pole, shaft, or quant.

STAIRCASE LOCKS, (also called RISERS), a flight or series of locks so arranged that the top gate or gates, of each lock, with the exception of the highest one, also form the bottom gate, or gates, of the lock above. See also chapter on locks.

STAITH, in the Midlands and North of England a staith is a place where coal is loaded into vessels; in the Norfolk district, it is the term for any kind of wharf.

STANDS, the intermediate supports for the gang planks of a narrow boat.

STANK, a temporary water-tight dam constructed of sheet piling out of which the water is pumped enabling repairs to be carried out.

STAUNCH, see FLASH LOCK.

STEAMERS, a term for early motor narrow boats powered by steam engines.

STEERER, the controller of a narrow boat.

STOP, a stop, or stop lock, is generally a lock or gates, erected at the junction of one canal with another, in order to prevent the loss of water between canals. There was usually a toll office at a stop lock where cargoes were declared, boats gauged and tolls paid. The term STOP was sometimes used to denote a toll office not adjoining another canal company's property, as on the Birmingham Canal Navigation.

STOP GATES, an improvement on the idea of stop planks; gates placed at intervals along the waterway and normally kept open, but which can be shut when required to isolate a stretch of canal containing a breach or requiring repair.

STOP GROOVES and PLANKS, the vertical grooves, usually provided at the head and tail of each lock, and in other situations as required, into which stop planks can be inserted to form a temporary dam.

Above Stop planks in readiness on the canal bank
Below Stop planks in position, sealing the entrance to a lock under repair

STRAP or CHECK STRAP, a rope used for the purpose of stopping a vessel, one end being made fast on board and the other twisted round a stump, a bollard or other suitable object on shore.

STRETCHER, detachable planks or chains fitted across the hold of a narrow boat to keep the hull rigid, and to prevent the sides from being forced out when loaded.

STUD, in use on narrow boats, a loose iron pin with a 'T' head fitting into a socket, to which towing and mooring lines are made fast. Studs are named according to their position on the boat: fore studs, stern studs, and towing studs. Towing studs fit into a socket on the cabin top, and are used for attaching the long tow line necessary on some rivers, or when in tow of a tug. The position for the towing stud is selected in order that the line may be under the immediate control of the steerer. Before towing studs were brought into use, straight pins with a shoulder, called 'Soar Pins', were used in the same position and for the same purpose. The disadvantage of soar pins was that their use necessitated the towing line being fastened round the pin, both inside the cabin and outside, thereby chafing the combing of the cabin hatchway.

SUMMIT LEVEL, the highest pound of water in a canal; that pound into which the main water supply of the canal is directed.

SWEEP, a large oar used to propel and steer a lighter or dumb barge.

TACKLE, a boatman's term for the harness of a boat horse.

TOLL, (also called TONNAGE) the charge payable to a canal company for the use of the canal by a trader, or other person doing his own haulage.

TOW, an American term for a large number of dumb barges pushed or pulled by a single propulsion unit.

TOWPATH, the path by the side of a navigation used by towing horses: also called in various localities 'Hauling Path', and 'Haling Way', the latter being a Fen term.

TROW, a type of sailing vessel once in general use on the River Severn.

TUB BOATS, small box boats carrying from three to five tons each and usually worked in trains; now extinct; 'Tub Boat' canals were built to the small dimensions of the boats, principally in the West of England and Wales, and lifts and inclined planes were tried in place of locks. See also the chapter on locks.

TURNOVER BRIDGE, see ROVING BRIDGE.

TURNS, WAITING TURNS or WORKING TURNS, a system used in locking whereby one boat proceding in any direction has to wait for a boat coming the opposite way before passing through a lock, thus ensuring the maximum usage of the smallest amount of water.

TYING POINT, the shallowest point in a navigation or route of navigation; a boat being able to pass the tying point is thus able to use the whole navigation.

WEIGH DOCK, a dock used for the purpose of gauging a boat. See also GAUGING.

WEIR, an artificial barrier holding back water for navigation purposes; the change of level effected by the weir is overcome by means of a lock.

WHEEL, or LOCK WHEEL is to travel ahead of a boat making sure that all the locks are set in its favour, thereby speeding its passage. A person who does this is known as a 'Lock Wheeler'.

WHERRY, a type of vessel once commonly trading on Norfolk rivers.

WIDE BOAT, a type of boat used on some canals of a size intermediate between that of a narrow boat and a barge.

WIND, to wind a boat is to turn a boat round.

WINDING HOLE, WINDING PLACE, WINNING HOLE or WINNING PLACE, a wide place in a canal provided for the purpose of turning a boat round.

WINDLASS, (also called a CRANK or LOCK KEY), a square socket fitted with a handle and used for opening and closing lock paddles.

WINGS, the boards rigged for the purpose of legging through tunnels. See also the chapter on tunnels. NARROW CUT WINGS and BROAD CUT WINGS are used respectively in narrow and broad tunnels.

WOOLLY BACKED 'UNS, a derogatory name given by horse boat men to the crews of the early steamers operating from City Road Basin to Leicester and Nottingham and presumably derived from the Leicestershire woollen trade. Crews on the London to Birmingham steamers were similarly called GREASY OCKERS and GREASY WHEELERS, terms connected with the cargoes of soap which they often carried, and with the fact that the office of the Company was at Ocker Hill, Birmingham.

One of Brindley's circular weirs on the Staffordshire and Worcestershire Canal

Canal Tunnels in England and Wales

Name of Tunnel	Name of Canal	Length in yards	Remarks
Standege	Huddersfield Narrow	5415	Engineer Benjamin Outram Opened 1811 Canal abandoned 1944 Tunnel passable
Strood	Thames & Medway	3909	Engineer William T. Clark Opened 1824 Divided into two sections of 1530 yards and 2329 yards, c. 1825 Gravesend & Rochester Railway opened through the tunnel in 1845
Sapperton	Thames & Severn	3817	Engineer Josiah Clowes Opened 1789 Closed 1911
Lappal	Dudley (Birmingham Canal Navigations)	3795	Engineer William Underhill Opened 1798 Closed 1917
Dudley	Dudley (BCN)	3172	Engineers Thomas Dadford Snr. Isaac Pratt, Josiah Clowes Opened 1792 Canal and tunnel restored and reopened 1970s
Blisworth	Grand Junction (now Grand Union)	3056	Engineer James Barnes Opened 1805
Netherton	Birmingham Canal	3027	Engineer James Walker Opened 1858 Towpaths both sides first lit by gas, later electricity
Butterley	Cromford	2966	Engineers William Jessop, Benjamin Outram Lengthened to 3063 yards c. 1845 Opened 1794 Closed 1900
Harecastle (New)	Trent & Mersey	2926	Engineer Thomas Telford Opened 1827 Towpath
Harecastle (Old)	Trent & Mersey	2880	Engineers James Brindley, Hugh Henshall Opened 1777 Closed c. 1918

Name of Tunnel	Name of Canal	Length in yards	Remarks
Norwood	Chesterfield	2850	Engineers James Brindley, John Varley, Hugh Henshall Lengthened to 3102 yards c. 1848 Opened 1775 Closed 1908
West Hill	Worcester & Birmingham	2726	Engineer Thomas Cartwright Opened 1797
Morwelldown	Tavistock	2560	Engineer John Taylor Opened 1817 Closed c. 1889 Re-opened 1933 with part of the canal for the purpose of providing water supply
Oxenhall	Herefordshire & Gloucestershire	2192	Engineers Josiah Clowes, Robert Whitworth Opened 1798 Closed 1881
Braunston	Grand Junction (Now Grand Union)	2042	Engineer William Jessop Opened 1796
Crimson Hill	Chard	1800	Engineer Sidney Hall Opened 1839 Closed 1867
Foulridge	Leeds & Liverpool	1640	Engineer Robert Whitworth Opened 1796
Crick	Grand Union	1528	Engineer Benjamin Bevan Opened 1814
Southnet	Leominster	1250	Engineer Thomas Dadford Jnr Completed 1795 but never used
Preston Brook	Trent & Mersey	1239	Engineers James Brindley, Hugh Henshall Opened 1775
Greywell	Basingstoke	1200	Contractor John Pinkerton Opened 1796 Collapsed 1934
Husbands Bosworth	Grand Union	1166	Engineer Benjamin Bevan Opened 1813
Berwick	Shrewsbury	970	Engineer Josiah Clowes Opened 1797 Towpath added by William Reynold, but removed 1819 Closed 1936

Name of Tunnel	Name of Canal	Length in yards	Remarks
Islington	Regents	960	Engineer James Morgan Opened 1820
Fenny Compton	Oxford	(a) 336 (b) 452	Engineer Samuel Simcock Opened 1778 Tunnels separated by an opening 155 yards Tunnels removed c. 1870
Saddington	Leicestershire & Northamptonshire Union	880	Engineer John Varley Opened 1797
Southampton	Salisbury & Southampton	880	Engineer Joseph Hill 850 yards cut by 1802 Never completed
Shortwood	Worcester & Birmingham	613	Engineer Thomas Cartwright Opened 1807
Tardebigge	Worcester & Birmingham	580	Engineers Thomas Cartwright, John Woodhouse Opened 1810
Barnton	Trent & Mersey	572	Engineer Hugh Henshall Opened 1777
Gannow	Leeds & Liverpool	559	Engineer Robert Whitworth
Gosty Hill	Dudley (BCN)	557	Engineer William Underhill Opened 1798 Closed 1917
Bruce	Kennet & Avon	502	Engineer John Rennie Opened 1810 Chains on side wall for boatmen to haul on
Chirk	Ellesmere (now Welsh Canal)	459	Towpath
	Manchester & Salford Junction	440	Termination of canal under streets Footpath, but not towpath, in tunnel beside the canal
Aylestone Hill	Herefordshire & Gloucestershire	440	
Shrewley	Warwick & Birmingham (now Grand Union)	433	Handles on side wall for boatmen to haul on
Saltersford	Trent & Mersey	424	
Walsopthorne	Herefordshire & Gloucestershire	400	

Name of Tunnel	Name of Canal	Length in yards	Remarks
Hincaster	Lancaster	377	Rope on side wall for boatmen to haul on
Ashford	Brecon & Abergavenny	375	
Hardham	River Arun Navigation (Arun-Rother Junction Canal)	375	
Coseley	BCN	360	Towpath on both sides
King's Norton	Stratford-on-Avon	352	Handrail on side wall for boatmen to haul on
Putnel Field	Leominster	330	
Hyde Bank	Peak Forest	308	
Stirchley	Shropshire	281	
Snedshill	Shropshire	279	
Maida Hill	Regents	272	
Newbold (new)	Oxford	250	Opened 1834 to supersede old tunnel as part of canal shortening. Towpath both sides
Snarestone	Ashby-de-la-Zouch	250	
Dunhampstead	Worcester & Birmingham	230	Handrail on side wall for boatmen to haul on
Scout	Huddersfield Narrow	220	Towpath
Whitehouses	Ellesmere (now Welsh)	191	Towpath
Woodley	Peak Forest	167	Towpath
Drakeholes	Chesterfield	154	
Bury	Manchester, Bolton & Bury	141	
Newport	Monmouthshire	140	
Armitage	Trent & Mersey	130	Towpath now opened up
Leek	Leek Branch, Trent & Mersey	130	
Newbold (old)	Oxford	125	Towpath Replaced 1834
Cardiff	Glamorganshire	115	Towpath for 70 267 ft chains on side wall for boatmen to haul on

Name of Tunnel	Name of Canal	Length in yards	Remarks
Waterhouses	Hollinwood Branch, Ashton	110	Opened out c. 1920
Edgbaston	Worcester & Birmingham	105	Towpath
Hag	Cromford	93	Towpath
Cwmbran	Monmouthshire	87	
Ellesmere	Ellesmere (now Welsh)	87	Towpath
Cowley	Birmingham & Liverpool Junction (now Shropshire Union)	81	Towpath
Knott Mill	Rochdale	78	Towpath
Froghall	Caldon Branch, Trent & Mersey	76	
Gregory	Cromford	76	Towpath
Brewin's	BCN	75	Opened out c. 1857
Combe Hay	Somerset Coal	66	Railway opened through tunnel in 1910
Cookley	Staffordshire & Worcestershire	65	Towpath
Bath No. 1	Kennet & Avon	59	Towpath
Curdworth	Birmingham & Fazeley	57	Towpath
Brettel Lane	Stourbridge	56	Towpath: Opened out
Bath No. 2	Kennet & Avon	55	Towpath
No. 2, Salford	Manchester, Bolton & Bury	50	
Sowerby Long Bridge	Rochdale	43	Towpath
Alton	Uttoxeter Branch, Trent & Mersey	40	
No. 1, Salford	Manchester, Bolton & Bury	34	
Buckland Hollow	Cromford	33	Towpath
Little Tunnel Bridge	Basingstoke	33	Towpath
Wolfhampcote	Oxford	33	

The following very short tunnels, all under 30 yards, have also been built:

Ashted on the Birmingham Canal Navigations
Cricklade on the North Wilts. Branch of the Wiltshire & Berkshire Canal
Ilminster on the Chard Canal
Ketley on the Ketley Canal
Lillesdon on the Chard Canal
Neath on the Neath Canal
Newham on the Leominster Canal
Newport on the Mommouthshire Canal
Oakengates on the Shropshire Canal
Ocker Hill on the BCN Canal
Stourton on the Staffordshire & Worcestershire Canal

Principal Water Routes in England and Wales

TABLE A
Primary Inland Waterway Routes across England, connecting Liverpool to Hull, and London to Birmingham and Bristol

Route 1: London to Birmingham
Grand Union Canal

Route 2: Birmingham to Sharpness, for Bristol
Worcester & Birmingham Canal, and Severn Waterway

Route 3: London to Bristol
River Thames, and Kennet & Avon Navigation

Route 4: Hull to Liverpool – narrow canal route
River Humber, River Trent, Trent & Mersey Canal, Bridgewater Canal, and Leeds & Liverpool Canal

Route 5: Liverpool to Hull – broad canal route
Leeds & Liverpool Canal, Aire & Calder Navigation, Ouse Navigation, and River Humber

TABLE B
Junction Routes, running north/south, interconnecting the Four Ports and the Midlands

Route 6: Norton Junction to River Trent, for London to Hull
Leicestershire Section, Grand Union Canal

Route 7: Fradley Junction to Birmingham and Braunston Junction, for 'Cross' routes
Coventry, Birmingham, and Northern Oxford Canals

Route 8: Middlewich to Worcester, for Liverpool to Sharpness and Bristol
Shropshire Union and Staffordshire & Worcestershire Canals, and Severn Waterway

TABLE C
Secondary Canals, not on the major through routes, but notable for their amenity value and used principally for pleasure cruising

Route 9: Kidsgrove to Whaley Bridge
Macclesfield and Peak Forest Canals

Route 10: Napton Junction to Oxford
Southern Oxford Canal

Route 11: Hurleston Junction to Llantysilio
Welsh Canal

TABLE D
Manchester Ship Canal

Route 12: River Mersey to Manchester

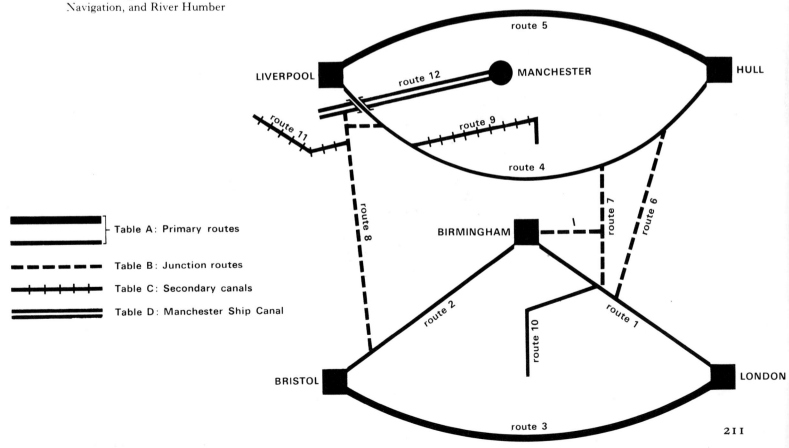

— Table A: Primary routes
Table B: Junction routes
Table C: Secondary canals
Table D: Manchester Ship Canal

In Tables A and B are set out the most direct lines of water communication between the major English ports of Liverpool, Hull, London, and Bristol; such communication is the fulfilment of Brindley's vision of a viable commercial canal system. The navigations listed in Table C were also envisaged as trade routes; their scenic geography, however, has assured their particular popularity with the traffic of a leisure-orientated age. The Manchester Ship Canal, the commercial giant of Britain's waterways, occupies Table D. In all tables, running distances are measured in miles from major canal junctions and ports.

TABLE A
Primary Inland Waterway Routes

Route 1: London to Birmingham
Grand Union Canal

Maximum size of craft on through route: 72 ft length, 7 ft beam
3 ft 6 in draught, 7 ft 6 in headroom
(Craft of 12 ft 6 in beam may navigate to Sampson Road by previous arrangement with British Waterways Board)
Navigation Authority: British Waterways Board
The main Line of the Grand Union Canal extends south to join the River Thames at Brentford.
Distance, Bulls Bridge, junction with Paddington Arm, to Brentford: 6 miles, 12 locks.

The Stratford-on-Avon Canal (Northern) connects the Grand Union Canal to the Worcester and Birmingham Canal, providing a through route from London to Bristol.
Distance, Kingswood, junction with Grand Union Canal, to Kings Norton, junction with Worcester and Birmingham Canal: 12½ miles, 19 locks

	Distances	
	miles	locks
PADDINGTON ARM		
London (City Road Basin) to :		
Bulls Bridge, junction with main line	17½	5
MAIN LINE		
Packet Boat Lane, junction with Slough Arm	21	5
Marsworth, junction with Aylesbury Arm	51	52
Blisworth Tunnel	84	77
Gayton, junction with Northampton Arm	88	77
Norton, junction with Leicestershire Section	101	84
Braunston Tunnel	102½	84
Braunston, junction with Northern Oxford Canal	105	90
Napton, junction with Southern Oxford Canal	110	90
Hatton flight of 21 locks	124½	115
Kingswood, junction with Stratford-on-Avon Canals	131½	136
Birmingham, Sampson Road; terminus of wide-lock navigation	145	141
Birmingham Canals		
Birmingham, Gas Street Basin	148	167

Route 2: Birmingham to Sharpness, for Bristol
Worcester & Birmingham Canal, and Severn
Waterway

Maximum size of craft on through route: 71 ft 6 in length, 7 ft beam, 3 ft 3 in draught, approx. 6 ft headroom
Navigation Authority: (to Sharpness) British Waterways Board

	Distances	
	miles	locks
WORCESTER & BIRMINGHAM CANAL		
Birmingham, Gas Street Basin to :		
Kings Norton, junction with Stratford-on-Avon Canal	5½	
West Hill Tunnel	6	
Tardebigge flight of 30 locks	14	
Worcester, junction with Severn Waterways	30	58
RIVER SEVERN NAVIGATION		
Tewkesbury, junction with Lower Avon Navigation	46	59
Gloucester, junction with Gloucester & Sharpness Canal	59	61
GLOUCESTER & SHARPNESS CANAL		
Saul, junction with Stroudwater Canal (disused, except for mooring)	67	61
Sharpness, junction with Severn Estuary	75½	61
SEVERN ESTUARY		
Bristol, Avonmouth, junction with River Avon	125	61

Route 3: London to Bristol
River Thames, and Kennet & Avon Navigation

Maximum size of craft on through route (theoretical): 73 ft length, 13 ft 10 in beam, 3 ft 6 in draught, 8 ft 6 in headroom
Navigation Authorities: Port of London Authority to Teddington; Thames Conservancy to High Bridge, Reading; British Waterways Board to Hanham; Port of Bristol Authority to Avonmouth
Kennet & Avon route impassable to through traffic, 1977, but eventual restoration is likely

	Distances	
	miles	locks
RIVER THAMES		
Brentford (junction with Grand Union Canal, main line) to :		
Teddington Locks, end of tidal section	5	
Shepperton, junction with River Wey	16½	3
Reading junction with River Kennet	59½	20
RIVER KENNET		
Reading, High Bridge	60½	21
Burghfield Lock	64	24
Newbury Wharf, start of Kennet & Avon Canal	79	42
KENNET & AVON CANAL		
Devizes, flight of 29 locks	114	77
Bath, start of River Avon section	136	121
RIVER AVON		
Hanham, end of Kennet & Avon Navigation	147	127
BRISTOL AVON		
Avonmouth, junction with Severn Estuary	161	129

Route 4: Hull to Liverpool – narrow canal route
River Humber, River Trent, Trent & Mersey Canal, Bridgewater Canal, and Leeds & Liverpool Canal

Maximum size of craft on through route: 72 ft length, 7 ft beam, 2 ft 9 in draught, 5 ft 9 in headroom
Navigation Authorities: Humber Conservancy to Gainsborough; British Waterways Board to Liverpool

	Distances miles	locks
HUMBER CONSERVANCY		
Hull to :		
Trent Falls, junction with Ouse Navigation	16½	
Gainsborough	42½	
RIVER TRENT		
Torksey, junction with Fossdyke & Witham Navigation	52½	
Cromwell Lock, end of tidal section	68½	
Cranfleet Cut, junction with Grand Union Canal, Leicestershire Section, and Erewash Canal	107½	11
Derwent Mouth, junction with Trent & Mersey Canal	109½	13
TRENT & MERSEY CANAL		
Dallow Lane Lock, limit of wide-lock navigation	126½	19
Fradley, junction with Coventry Canal	135½	30
Great Haywood, junction with Staffordshire & Worcestershire Canal	148	35
Etruria Summit, junction with Caldon Canal (closed but navigable for light craft)	166½	53
Harecastle Tunnel	170	53
Kidsgrove, junction with Macclesfield Canal	172½	53
Middlewich, junction with Shropshire Union Canal	184½	84
Anderton, junction with River Weaver via boat lift	194½	88
Preston Brook, tunnel, and junction with Bridgewater Canal	201½	89
BRIDGEWATER CANAL		
Stretford, junction with Leigh Branch	222½	89
Barton Swing Aqueduct	225	89
Leigh, junction with Leeds & Liverpool Canal, Leigh Branch	235½	89
LEEDS & LIVERPOOL CANAL, LEIGH BRANCH		
Wigan, junction with main line	243	93
LEEDS & LIVERPOOL CANAL, MAIN LINE		
Burscough, junction with Rufford Branch	253½	99
Liverpool, Lightbody Street, Stanley Docks Junction	277½	99

Route 5: Liverpool to Hull – broad canal route
Leeds & Liverpool Canal, Aire & Calder Navigation, Ouse Navigation, and River Humber

Maximum size of craft on through route: 62 ft length, 14 ft beam, 3 ft 9 in draught, 8 ft headroom
Navigation Authorities: British Waterways Board to Trent Falls; Humber Conservancy to Hull

	Distances miles	locks
LEEDS & LIVERPOOL CANAL		
Liverpool, Lightbody Street (Stanley Docks Junction) to :		
Burscough, junction with Rufford Branch	24	
Wigan, junction with Leigh Branch	34½	6
Wheelton, junction with Walton Summit Branch, formerly Lancaster Canal	46½	27
Burnley Embankment	73	40
Foulridge Tunnel	80½	47
Leeds, River Lock, junction with Aire & Calder Navigation	126½	91
AIRE & CALDER NAVIGATION		
Castleford, junction with Calder & Hebble Navigation	134½	98
Bank Dole, junction with Selby Canal	141½	101
Junction with New Junction Canal	151	103
Goole, junction with Ouse Navigation	158½	104
OUSE NAVIGATION		
Trent Falls, junction with River Humber	166½	104
RIVER HUMBER		
Hull	183	104

TABLE B
Junction Routes

Route 6: Norton Junction to River Trent, for London to Hull.
Leicestershire Section, Grand Union Canal

Maximum size of craft on junction route: 72 ft length, 7 ft beam, 3 ft 6 in draught, 7 ft headroom
Maximum size of craft on London to Hull through route: as above
Navigation Authority: British Waterways Board

	Distances miles	locks
Norton (junction with Grand Union Canal, main line) to :		
Watford Staircase Locks	2½	2
Avon Aqueduct, junction with Welford Arm	15½	7
Foxton Staircase Locks (site of inclined plane)	23	7
Foxton, junction with Market Harborough Arm	23½	17
Leicester	41	41
Cranfleet Cut, junction with Trent Waterway and Erewash Canal	66	59

Route 7: Fradley Junction to Birmingham and Braunston Junction, for 'Cross' routes
Coventry, Birmingham, and Northern Oxford Canals

Maximum size of craft on Hull to Birmingham and Bristol through routes: as above

Maximum size of craft on Liverpool to Birmingham and London
through routes: 72 ft length, 7 ft beam, 2 ft 9 in draught, 5 ft 9 in
headroom
Navigation Authority: British Waterways Board

	Distances	
	miles	locks
COVENTRY CANAL		
Fradley (junction with Trent & Mersey Canal) to :		
Fazeley, junction with Birmingham & Fazeley Canal	11	
BIRMINGHAM CANALS		
Birmingham, Gas Street Basin	28½	38
Coventry Canal, Fradley Junction, to :		
Marston, junction with Ashby-de-la-Zouch Canal	30½	13
Hawkesbury, junction with Oxford Canal,		
Northern line	33½	13
OXFORD CANAL, NORTHERN		
Rugby	47½	14
Braunston, junction with Grand Union Canal,		
main line	58	17

Route 8: Middlewich to Worcester, for Liverpool to Sharpness and Bristol
Shropshire Union and Staffordshire & Worcestershire Canals, and Severn Waterway
Maximum size of craft on junction route, and on Liverpool to Bristol
through route: 70 ft length, 7 ft beam, 3 ft draught, 7 ft 6 in headroom
Navigation Authority: British Waterways Board.

	Distances	
	miles	locks
SHROPSHIRE UNION CANAL		
Ellesmere Port (junction with Manchester Ship		
Canal) to :		
Chester, River Dee Branch	8½	2
Barbridge, junction with Middlewich Branch	24½	16
MIDDLEWICH BRANCH		
Middlewich (junction with Trent & Mersey		
Canal) to :		
Barbridge, junction with main line	10	4
MAIN LINE		
Hurleston, junction with Welsh Canal	11	4
Audlem flight of 15 locks	19	6
Norbury, junction with disused Shrewsbury Canal	36½	31
Autherley, junction with Staffordshire &		
Worcestershire Canal	52	33
STAFFORDSHIRE & WORCESTERSHIRE CANAL		
Aldersley, junction with Birmingham Canal	52½	33
Stourton, junction with Stourbridge Canal	65	51
Stourport-on-Severn, junction with Severn		
Waterway	77½	65
RIVER SEVERN		
Worcester, junction with Worcester & Birmingham		
Canal	90	68

TABLE C
Secondary Canals

Route 9: Kidsgrove to Whaley Bridge
Macclesfield and Peak Forest Canals
Maximum size of craft to Whaley Bridge: 70 ft length, 7 ft beam,
2 ft 9 in draught, 6 ft headroom
Navigation Authority: British Waterways Board

	Distances	
	miles	locks
MACCLESFIELD CANAL		
Kidsgrove (junction with Trent & Mersey Canal) to :		
Bosley flight of 12 locks	10	1
Macclesfield	16	13
Marple, junction with Peak Forest Canals	27	13
UPPER PEAK FOREST CANAL		
Whaley Bridge, canal terminus, and junction		
with Buxworth Arm	33	13

Route 10: Napton Junction to Oxford
Southern Oxford Canal
Maximum size of craft to Oxford: 70 ft length, 7 ft beam, 3 ft 6 in
draught, 7 ft headroom
Navigation Authority: British Waterways Board

	Distances	
	miles	locks
Napton (junction with Grand Union Canal) to :		
Engine House Arm	3	14
Marston Doles, summit lock	4	16
Claydon Top Lock, end of summit pound	14½	16
Banbury	22	29
Duke's Cut (to River Thames)	47	44
Oxford, junction with River Thames	50	46

Route 11: Hurleston Junction to Llantysilio
Welsh Canal
Maximum size of craft to Llantysilio: 72 ft length, 6 ft 10 in beam,
2 ft draught, 6 ft headroom
Navigation Authority: British Waterways Board

	Distances	
	miles	locks
Hurleston (junction with Shropshire Union Canal) to :		
Prees Branch (closed)	19½	18
Ellesmere Turn	25½	18
Ellesmere Wharf	26	18
Frankton, junction with old Montgomeryshire		
Canal (closed)	29	18
Chirk Aqueduct, Welsh border	36	20
Pont-y-Cysyllte Aqueduct	39½	20
Ruabon, start of navigable feeder		
(not recommended for large craft)	40	20

TABLE D
Manchester Ship Canal

Route 12: River Mersey to Manchester

Maximum size of vessels to Manchester: 600 ft length, 65 ft beam, 28 ft draught, 70 ft headroom

Navigation Authority: Manchester Ship Canal Company

	Distances	
	miles	locks
Eastham Locks, (junction with River Mersey) to :		
Ellesmere Port, junction with Shropshire Union Canal	$3\frac{1}{4}$	1
Weston Point, junction with River Weaver	$10\frac{3}{4}$	1
Weston Mersey Side Lock, junction with River Mersey	$10\frac{3}{4}$	1
Runcorn Docks	12	1
Runcorn Side Lock, junction with River Mersey	13	1
Latchford Locks	21	1
Irlam Locks	$28\frac{1}{2}$	2
Barton Locks	$30\frac{1}{2}$	3
Barton Swing Aqueduct	$31\frac{3}{4}$	4
Mode Wheel Locks	34	4
MANCHESTER		
Salford Quay	34	5
Trafford Wharf	$34\frac{1}{4}$	5
Manchester Docks, 9, 8, 7 and 6	$34\frac{1}{4}$	5
Manchester Docks, 4, 3, 2 and 1	$35\frac{1}{2}$	5
Head of Ship Canal, junction with River Irwell	36	5

Selected Bibliography

Historical Works and Canal Histories

Anon
The History of Inland Navigation, 1776

Boyes, John and Russell, Ronald
The Canals of Eastern England Newton Abbot, 1977
Broadbridge, S. R.
The Birmingham Canal Navigations, Vol. 1 (1768–1846) Newton Abbot, 1974

Clew, Kenneth R.
The Kennet & Avon Canal Newton Abbot, 1968
The Somersetshire Coal Canal and Railways Newton Abbot, 1970
The Dorset and Somerset Canal Newton Abbot, 1971
Compton, Hugh J.
The Oxford Canal Newton Abbot, 1976

Dalby, J.
The Wilts and Berks Canal Lingfield, 1971

Faulkner, Alan H.
The Grand Junction Canal Newton Abbot, 1972

Gladwin, D. D. and White, J. M.
English Canals, Part 1 : A Concise History Lingfield, 1968

Hadfield, Charles
British Canals – An Illustrated History London, 1950
The Canals of Southern England London, 1955
The Canals of South Wales and the Border London and Cardiff, 1960
The Canals of the East Midlands Newton Abbot, 1966
The Canals of the West Midlands Newton Abbot, 1966
The Canals of South West England Newton Abbot, 1967
The Canals of South and South East England Newton Abbot, 1969
The Canals of Yorkshire and North-East England (2 volumes) Newton Abbot, 1972/73
Hadfield, Charles and Norris, John
Waterways to Stratford London, 1962
Hadfield, Charles and Briddle, Gordon
The Canals of North West England (2 volumes) Newton Abbot, 1970
Harris, Helen
The Grand Western Canal Newton Abbot, 1973
Harris, Helen and Ellis, Monica
The Bude Canal Newton Abbot, 1972
Household, Humphrey
The Thames and Severn Canal Newton Abbot, 1969

Phillips, J.
A General History of Inland Navigation, Foreign and Domestic London, 1792
Pratt, E. A.
British Canals : Is their Resuscitation Practicable London, 1906
Priestley, Joseph
Historical Accounts of the Navigable Rivers, Canals and Railways throughout Great Britain London, 1831

Spencer, Herbert
London's Canal London, 1961
Stevens, Philip
The Leicester Line Newton Abbot, 1972
Stevenson, Peter
The Nutbrook Canal Newton Abbot, 1970

Thacker, Fred S.
The Thames Highway : General History London, 1914
The Thames Highway : Locks and Weirs London, 1920

Vine, P. A. L.
London's Lost Route to the Sea Newton Abbot, 1965
London's Lost Route to Basingstoke Newton Abbot, 1969

Welch, Edwin
The Bankrupt Canal Southampton, 1966
Willan, Thomas S.
River Navigation in England 1600–1750 Oxford, 1936
Report of the Royal Commission on Canals London, 1906–10

Canal Architecture, Engineering and Construction

Boucher, Cyril
John Rennie Manchester, 1963
Burton, Anthony
The Canal Builders London, 1969

Chappell, Metius
British Engineers London, 1942

Dickinson, H. W.
Robert Fulton, Engineer and Artist London, 1913

Fulton, Robert
A Treatise on Improvement of Canal Navigation London, 1796

Gibb, Sir Alexander
The Story of Telford, London, 1935
Gladwin, D. D. and White, J. M.
English Canals Part II : Engineers and Engineering Lingfield, 1968

Malet, Hugh
The Canal Duke London, 1961

Nettleford, J. S.
Garden Cities and Canals London, 1914

Pownal, J. F.
The Projected Grand Contour Canal Birmingham, 1942
Pratt, Frances
Canal Architecture in Britain 1976

Rolt, L. T. C.
Thomas Telford Harlow, 1958
Navigable Waterways Harlow, 1969
Ransom, P. J. G.
Waterways Restored London, 1974

Smiles, Samuel
Lives of the Engineers (Volumes I and II) London, 1861

Vince, John
Canals and Canal Architecture Shire Alum No. 3, 1972

Boats and Boat People

Chaplin, Tom
A Short History of the Narrow Boat 1973

Frere-Cook, Gervis (ed.) and McKnight, Hugh
Decorative Arts of the Mariner London, 1966
Fairbairn, Sir William
Remarks on Canal Navigation Illustrative of the Advantages of the Use of Steam as a Moving Power on Canals London, 1831

Gladwin, D. D. and White, J. M.
English Canals Part III : Boats and Boatmen Lingfield, 1969

Lansdell, Avril
The Clothes of the Cut – A History of Canal Costume London, 1975
Lewery, A. J.
Narrow Boat Painting Newton Abbot, 1974

O'Connor, John
Canals, Barges and People London, 1950

Rolt, L. T. C.
Narrow Boat London, 1944

Smith, D. J.
Canal Boats and Boaters London, 1973
Smith, George
Our Canal Population – 'A Cry from the Boat Cabins' – With Remedy London, 1875

Wilson, Robert J.
The Number Ones Kettering, 1972

Travelogues, Maps and Guides

Bliss, W
The Heart of England by Waterway London, 1933
Bonthron, P.
My Holidays on Inland Waterways London, 1916

Dashwood, J. B.
The Thames to the Solent by Canal and Sea or the Log of the Una Boat 'Caprice' London, 1868

McKnight, Hugh
The Shell Book of Inland Waterways Newton Abbot, 1975

Nicholson's Guides to the Waterways : South-West, South-East, North-West, North-East (4 volumes) London, 1971–73

de Salis, H. R.
Chronology of Inland Navigation London, 1897
Bradshaw's Guide to the Canals and Navigable Rivers of England and Wales London, 1904

Stanford, Edward
Stanford's Inland Cruising Map of England for Larger Craft London, 1961

Thurston, E. Temple
Flower of Gloster London, 1911

Westall, G.
Inland Cruising on the Rivers and Canals of England and Wales London, 1908

Mainly Pictorial

Burton, Anthony and Pratt, Derek
Canals in Colour London, 1974

Gladwin, D. D.
Victorian and Edwardian Canals from Old Photographs London, 1976

McKnight, Hugh
Canal and River Craft in Pictures Newton Abbot, 1969

Ware, Michael E.
A Canalside Camera 1845–1930 Newton Abbot, 1975

General Reading

Aickman, Robert
The Story of Our Inland Waterways London, 1955

Burton, Anthony and Pratt, Derek
Canal Newton Abbot, 1976

Cadbury, G and Dobbs, S. P.
Canals and Inland Waterways London, 1929

Eyre, Frank and Hadfield, Charles
British Rivers and Canals Glasgow, 1942

Forbes, V. A. and Ashford, W. H. R.
Our Waterways London, 1906

Gladwin, D. D.
The Canals of Britain London, 1973
The Waterways of Britain – A Social Panorama London, 1976

Hadfield, Charles
Introducing Canals London, 1955
The Canal Age Newton Abbot, 1968

de Maré, Eric
Canals of England London, 1950

Rolt, L. T. C.
The Inland Waterways of England London, 1950
Russell, Ronald
Lost Canals of England and Wales Newton Abbot, 1971

Smith, Peter
Waterways Heritage 1971

Journals

Bulletin – Inland Waterways Association
Industrial Archeology
Journal of the Railway and Canal Historical Society
Navvies – Waterways Recovery Group
Waterways News – British Waterways Board
Waterways World

Index

This book is to be returned on or before
the last date stamped below.

10 MAY 1985

-6. DEC. 1993

3533
626
HARRIS, R

Canals and
their Architect

DG

3533